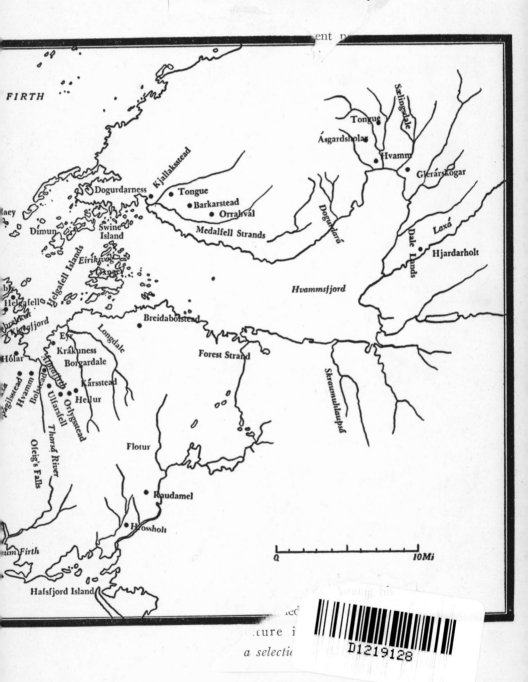

EYRBYGGJA SAGA

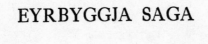

Translated from the Old Icelandic by PAUL SCHACH

Introduction and verse translations by LEE M. HOLLANDER

THE   UNIVERSITY   OF

AND   THE   AMERICAN - SC

EYRBYGGJA
SAGA

EBRASKA PRESS: 1959

INAVIAN FOUNDATION

Library of Congress Catalog Card No. 59-11221

Publishers on the Plains

UNP

To our Icelandic friends

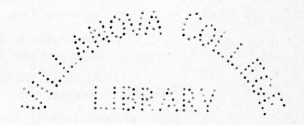

v

vi

PREFACE

The present translation is based on the editions of *Eyrbyggja saga* by Hugo Gering in the *Altnordische Saga-Bibliothek* (1897) and by Einar Ól. Sveinsson in the *Íslenzk Fornrit* series (1935). It was undertaken in the belief that a new translation was called for, our conceptions of the style of such a translation having changed since that of Morris and Magnússon in their Saga Library, Vol. II, 1892.

In addition to writing the Introduction and translating the verse material, Professor Hollander also collaborated, in general, in giving the book its present shape.

With regard to the Skaldic poetry here reproduced it should be borne in mind that this *genre* of Old Norse poetry has an archaic vocabulary radically different from prose; that its word order is free to an extraordinary degree; and hence that a translation obliterating these characteristics altogether would give an utterly false idea of that remarkable *genre*. Even so, only an approximation to its style is here attempted.

Thanks are due on the part of Professor Schach to the Research Council of the University of Nebraska for allotting to him a Faculty Research Fellowship for making preparatory studies of the saga; and to the American Philosophical Society for a grant to spend a summer in Iceland, there to study at the National Library in Reykjavík and by two visits to Snæfellsness and a sojourn of several weeks at Helgafell farm to acquaint himself with the locale of the saga. In connection with his stay in Iceland he expresses his gratitude to Chief Librarian Finnur Sigmundsson for the use of library facilities and to farmer Hinrik Jónsson and his wife, Ragnheidur Thorgeirsdóttir, for their hospitality. Assistance was lent him in the interpretation of difficult passages by Professor Einar Ól. Sveinsson of the University of Iceland, Librarian Agnar Thórdarson (Reykjavík), and Professor Stefán Einarsson of The Johns Hopkins University. For the arduous task of repeated typing his thanks are due to his wife, Mrs. Ruth Yohn Schach.

The treatment of Icelandic names is a notoriously difficult task requiring both experience and tact. Absolute consistency in either translating all names or leaving them all in their original form is unattainable. We have not hesitated to use hybrids like Haugsvad Ford, the Laxá River, etc., which, though horrendous to a person knowing Old Norse, will not be objectionable to the layman, any more than, say, the Orkney Islands or the Rio Grande River. The main point we conceive to be the comprehensibility of terms and the ease of identifying geographical names on the map.

The pronunciation of Icelandic names is not difficult if the reader will bear in mind that its vowels have the continental values; that *g* (as in Gísli, Ingjald) is always "hard"; and that the accent mark designates length, not stress (which invariably falls on the first syllable). *Y* (short or long) may be pronounced like *i* in *pin, mien,* the dipthongs *au* and *ei* (*ey*), as in *how* and *day* respectively. *J* has the value of *y* in *yes.*

The number of notes may seem excessive. Yet it has seemed to us an irreducible minimum, called for to explain conditions in, and allusions to, a civilization so far removed from ours. Needless to say, we are indebted for much in these notes to the learning of Eiríkur Magnússon, Hugo Gering and Einar Ól. Sveinsson in the translation and the editions mentioned above.

The map of Snæfellsness was based in large part on the maps by Helgi Sigurdsson, and the picture of Helgafell was suggested by the drawing by Tryggvi Magnússon in the edition of Einar Ól. Sveinsson. For permission to use these materials the translators express their appreciation to the artists and the publisher, *Hið íslenzka fornritafélag.*

We wish to express our appreciation also to the Committee on Publications of the American-Scandinavian Foundation, and especially to Dr. Henry Goddard Leach and Mr. Erik J. Friis, for their good services in furthering the publication of this book.

LMH
PS

CONTENTS

INTRODUCTION

To the modern reader the Old Icelandic "family sagas," i.e., sagas dealing with the lives of Icelanders, unquestionably have an air of sameness.
He carries away the general impression of bloody feuds, of many gene-
alogies, of the Icelandic fondness for litigation; and negatively, of the
small role erotic complications play in them. However, longer familiarity
and closer study reveal that after all such generalizations are hardly war-
ranted: in some, like *Laxdœla saga, Kormáks saga, Gunnlaugs saga,*
erotic relations do play a predominant role; in some, as in the *Gísla saga,*
legal proceedings are of minimal importance; in others there is little or
no bloodshed or litigation. And we shall discover that, apart from the
unmistakable "family likeness" produced by similar style and sameness
of social background and attitudes, they are by no means cut over the
same last; that, on the contrary, the diverse predilections and interests
of the various authors confer distinct individuality on the respective
sagas. *Eyrbyggja saga* is a case in point.

Walter Scott could not have made a better choice for his contribution
to Blackwell's well-known *Illustrations of Northern Antiquities* (1814)
than the generous excerpts culled for it by him from Thorkelin's Latin
translation of *Eyrbyggja saga* (1787). For in no other saga is there found
such a wealth of glimpses of the "antiquities"—that is, the beliefs, the
folkways, the traditions and manners—of the Norsemen of the tenth and
eleventh centuries, furnished by an author who, though writing centuries later, was deeply interested in the life of his ancestors—as so many
of his countrymen were and still are, to a degree that is characteristic
of the whole people. In fact, it is doubtful if any nation can match them
in that respect, notwithstanding the manifold cosmopolitan, alien diver-
sions and interests our age has imported into the once remote island.
No wonder, therefore, that *Eyrbyggja saga,* strongly set off by this
antiquarian interest, has been one of their favorites—even though it does
not sound the heights and depths of humanity as does, e.g., the *Njáls
saga,* the *Gísla saga,* the *Laxdœla saga,* and even though there is no con-

tinuous, absorbing narrative as in these and other great works of Icelandic antiquity, and the whole is built up of loosely connected episodes—so much so, in fact, that one may call it the most episodic of the longer sagas.*

Certainly, although there is much first-rate story-telling in the saga, the modern reader misses the close-knit structure he expects in a good novel. There is no "plot" or unity in our sense. Rather, as we are told at the end, it is "the saga of the Thórsnessings, the people of Eyr, and those of the Álptafjord"; the chronicle, that is, of a countryside, the story of the inhabitants of the long, mountainous peninsula of Snæfellsness, of their settlement in the new country, their feuds about prestige and property during the first century of their settling there, centering more or less around certain dominant clans and personalities.

Among these, in the third generation, Snorri becomes the most prominent and thus might seem to represent what we moderns instinctively look for, a central figure or "hero." But, far more realistically minded than we, the men of old knew that, as the Eddic *Fáfnismál* put it,

> When many are met
> to match their strength,
> 't will be found that foremost is no one;

and in this respect the sagas, and our saga in particular, are more true to actual life and history than our novels in which the action is made to revolve around a "hero."

As to Snorri, the action of the saga by no means revolves around him. On the contrary, in the beginning at least, Arnkel is his equal if not his superior—a born leader who by virtue of his resourcefuless, his forthrightness, his fighting ability, and other chieftainly qualities wins the loyalty of many followers. He is laid low through overconfidence in his own prowess—when discretion would have been the better part of valor —and the witlessness of a slave. Only when this dangerous rival has been removed does Snorri win the undisputed leadership. It is in capable hands. As the story develops, our respect for him grows, though perhaps not our sympathy. He is a Fabius Cunctator rather than a Hotspur, one who has the strength of mind not to be goaded into half-measures

---

*Since writing this I have come to a different conclusion; viz., that there is reason to think that the arrangement of the various seemingly disconnected "episodes" is due to deliberate planning by the author. See *Journal of English and Germanic Philology,* April 1959.

but to bide his time till he can strike the decisive blow, and then he is ruthless. He is a man of peace—when it suits his purposes; a peace-maker, not so much out of human kindness but because to be a successful mediator is a feather in his cap. Though not of commanding presence, a prime requisite for leadership in those rude days, he does not lack physical courage, and makes up for any lack of strength by his canniness and presence of mind. All in all, at least so far as our saga is concerned, not a man to admire, a shrewd politician and diplomat. In other sagas, to be sure, he is of a larger stature. In the *Njáls saga* he is called "the wisest man in Iceland of those who had not the gift of prophecy." And it is Snorri who at two critical junctures played a decisive role in the history of the republic—once, when the question whether to adopt Chris-tianity as the state religion threatened to disrupt the Althing; and again, when the suit over the burning of Njál almost led to civil war.

The criticism might be levelled at *Eyrbyggja* that—as is the case with most sagas—there are too many personages introduced (and too many with similar names) for us to get acquainted with in a book of such moderate size. But such criticism would not take into account the con-ditions of the times and the place of its origin. For, as in other peoples at the agricultural stage of cultural development, the knowledge of genealogy—nay, the relish of it—forms a very essential portion of the total mental contents of the community. In the remoter rural districts, everywhere, people know far more people, and more about them, than do the average city dwellers, who may live next door to one another for years without knowing their neighbors by name, let alone their family history, habits, character. But if there are many personages in *Eyr-byggja,* yet a fair number of them are drawn with such skill and knowl-edge of human nature that we are not apt to forget them. The most mem-orable figure, no doubt, is the old cantankerous curmudgeon, Thórólf, an admirable study of senile avarice and general churlishness, contrasted with the upright, calm fair-dealing of his son, Arnkel; whereas his daugh-ter, Geirríd, plainly has inherited much of her father's bile. No wonder she is out of patience with her son, the somewhat phlegmatic, peace-loving Thórarin who is well-mated with the gentle, self-effacing Aud. With only a few deft touches the author neatly outlines the pleasure- and finery-loving Thuríd, a regular courtesan type, a woman who betrays her husband without any compunction and can wheedle and wind him around her finger. To us she seems unworthy of the love of the knightly soldier of fortune, Bjorn. To her disadvantage we may contrast with her the desolate widow Thorgerd, sent from pillar to post and loyally carrying out barbarous advice to wring from Arnkel the promise to initiate suit against Snorri. Least satisfactory, because contradictory and vague, is the delineation of Thorgunna in the episode filled with macabre and grisly details which takes up a disproportionate amount of space in the saga but adds little to it.*

I have spoken of the author. As is the case with all Icelandic sagas the author of our saga is not known. Yet, as remarked before, he reveals his personality, his predilections and interests so clearly that it does not really matter whether we know his name. Still, they color his work so decisively, though perhaps not to its advantage as a narrative, that his authorship is of surpassing interest.

What manner of man was he? His work gives us many clues for our knowledge of him.

That he belonged to the upper class of society seems indicated by his scornfully humorous treatment of the dull, awkward, easily panicked slaves. He was clerically trained, of course; for how else, in that age, could he have received the training how to read and write—and he certainly had read a considerable number of manuscripts. Very likely he got this training at the Augustinian monastery located at his time on Helgafell. But in all probability he was not a clergyman himself: not only are there no pious reflections in his work, but Christianity in general evidently was not in the forefront of his thinking. It does not occur to him to have evil Thórólf's ghost in its final hauntings "laid" by churchly exorcism, though the land was long christianized in the writer's time. The same is true of Thorgunna's spooking. She is, to be sure, put by in the Skálaholt churchyard—"and when they [the pall bearers] came to Skálaholt, the precious things which she had willed to the church were delivered there, and the priests gladly received it all" (and some malice might be detected in that remark); but when her Christian burial does not prevent her spooking, and when things at Fróda get out of hand, what with the hauntings of the drowned Thórodd and his company, the revenants are finally evicted by a sort of juridical procedure, after which, to be sure, the attending priest performs the appropriate Christian rites. Not a single priest is mentioned by name in the saga, not even who first officiated in the churches at Fróda and Helgafell, which would certainly not have been the case if the author had been in any way connected with the Church; though true to his antiquarian in-

---

*Though it somehow attracted Robert Louis Stevenson enough for him to base his tale of "The Waif Woman" on it (*Scribner's,* 1914, Vol. 56, pp. 687-701).

terests he notes soberly (or ironically?) that these churches were built
by the chieftains because of the promise of the priests that as many could
be accommodated in the Kingdom of Heaven as could find standing room
in them, but that there were no priests as yet to perform the services in
such as were built. And so far as the progenitors of the Thórsnessings
are concerned, he shows no indignation at Bjorn Ketilsson who looks
down with scorn on his kin in the Hebrides for having abandoned the
faith of their forefathers.

Certain it is that no one but a native of the Snæfellsness Peninsula
could possibly have written our saga, one who knew literally every rock
and rill of that devious and difficult terrain, especially the northern
versant, from having lived and fared there for many years with an open
eye for its physical and historical features. No casual visitor could give
as accurate and detailed descriptions of localities and routes. And no
mistakes can be detected here.

Neither can any serious error be found in the author's historical and
genealogical information. His consuming interest in the "antiquities" of
his home land has made *Eyrbyggja* a veritable treasure trove for the folk-
lorist, the archeologist, the student of cults and traditions. Here we find
such precious information as the settlers' mode of selecting their dwelling-
place on the newly discovered island—how Thórólf Mostrarskegg, after
ascertaining the will of "his good friend, the god Thór," takes with him
on his ship, already loaded with kinsfolk, slaves, and chattels, the timber
of Thór's temple, together with the soil under the pediment of the altar;
how, on approaching Iceland, he throws overboard the pillars of his
highseat on which the image of the god was carved, to let Thór show
him where to settle. There follows the justly famous, and accurate,
description of the shrine he erects, its furnishings, and the ritual of the
sacrifice. We learn that the locality of the assembly on Thórsness is so
holy for him that it must in no way be desecrated, and that the mountain
of Helgafell on it becomes the abode of departed kinsmen to which a
later descendant is given a rousing welcome.

But it is not only matters of great moment the author deals with: it
interests him, as it certainly does us, to know that in those early times
tasseled shoestrings were in fashion, how people on board a ship managed about food and drink, and that all the household used to sit by the
warm kitchen fire before the evening meal.

In all these matters he exhibits the same scrupulous exactness of statement, the same reserve about an assertion, which leads him to say on
numerous occasions: "It is the opinion of some," "the rumor spread,"

"they say," and the like; and an intellectual honesty in judging motives which would do credit to a modern critical historian. All of which, of course, does not prevent him, in saga style (but also like historians of classical antiquity), from composing dialogues on occasions when the two interlocutors could not possibly be overheard by others—and they are always quick and pithy; nor from giving credence to the superstitions of his time.

The same qualities of mind are reflected in the author's style, and there chiefly in his pronounced tendency to understatement. The figure of *litotes* (understatement) is, to be sure, characteristic of saga style; but here it is carried almost to excess as when—to give but one example— the crew of the fleet sent out by King Harold to subdue the Western Islands on their return report to him "that they had not observed that Ketil [their admiral] was furthering the power of King Harold in those parts"; meaning of course the exact opposite.

Incidentally, few sagas throw such a clear light on the manner of their composition: at the desk, with manuscripts lying open before the author, who skilfully "pieces together" tidbits of local tradition and episodes from other sagas, weaving them into a historical context, and fortifying his narrative with verse handed down by word of mouth. Witness such bookish turns as "X, who will recur later in this saga" (which, note well, belongs to a different category from the frequent statement occur- ring in the literature that a certain person "now is out of the saga"), or "as was written above," or "he occurs also frequently in other sagas than this one"—phrases which reveal that the author was able to leaf for- ward and backward in his own manuscript.

As to the verse, it is thought that the practice of inserting it may have originated in the desire to lend color to, or else to bear out, the narrative of the saga by adducing the occasional verse of witnesses contemporary to the event or, still better, participants in it. Certainly the verse of the oldest sagas, such as that of Kormák, are unquestionably genuine, their style and emotional attitude matching that of the skalds speaking them, and their language showing the earmarks of antiquity, with the surround- ing prose often merely a paraphrase or explanation of the verse, and con- tributing little, if anything, beyond it. Later, with the pattern once estab- lished, skalds would undertake to add verses of their own, based *on* the narrative; so that late sagas like the *Njáls saga* and *Grettis saga* have practically only "spurious" stanzas—as can be easily shown by their language and style—elaborating on the narrative but adding nothing to *it*.

Such is not the case in our saga, which has a considerable number of

Skaldic stanzas. Most numerous (sixteen) are those attributed to Thórarin, who—quite believably—becomes a poet only when under severest emotional stress: a man of peace, he is goaded to fury when accused of thievery and reproached by his own mother as a coward for not immediately avenging the insult; and still more so when, after an indecisive skirmish, he discovers the severed hand of his wife Aud. But later, after he has slain his adversary, his mind is torn between exultation and regret. He feels revulsion over having shed blood but protests that it was done only under unbearable provocation. There is good, solid workmanship in Thórarin's verses, though they hardly reveal any original poetic gift.

That, by all means, is the case with the seven *vísur* attributed to Bjorn Breidvíkingr, all dealing with his infatuation with Snorri's half sister, Thuríd, wedded to a somewhat feckless husband. Like himself they evince an outgoing, exuberant, robust temperament and have lyrical quality of a high order. In fact, stanza 24—if properly interpreted— ranks high among erotic verse, a genre of which Old Icelandic literature has a not inconsiderable number.

There seems no good reason to question the genuineness of the two stanzas spoken by Thormód Trefilsson. Of course, we may doubt whether all this verse actually was improvised, composed on the spur of the moment, as the saga alleges; just as even the layman may question the genuineness of the two stanzas attributed to the berserkers, considering they are Swedes who could hardly have mastered the poetic language of Norway-Iceland, and of those put in the mouth of the old servant woman gifted with second-sight; which does not necessarily mean that they are of poor quality, whoever did compose them.

It is difficult to come to a conclusion as to the date of composition of our saga. Some scholars place it as early as ca. 1200, which would make it one of the very first of the great sagas; others put it as late as the middle of the thirteenth century, depending chiefly on their evaluation of loans from *Eyrbyggja* by other sagas and whether we shall take at their face value the statements of the author that certain sagas were in existence at his writing—statements which are regarded by some scholars as later additions. But there is nothing to substantiate this hypercritical assumption. It is the feeling of this writer that these statements agree well with the conscientious attitude of the author on other matters, especially the scrupulous care with which he differentiates between what he has from local tradition—"some say," "it was bruited about"—and what from written sources. Consider also that all manuscripts, so far as they go, contain these statements.

It is certain that the saga must have been in existence not later than the middle of the thirteenth century because of indications in it that republican institutions were then still in force: the island was brought under the sway of the King of Norway shortly thereafter. Also, when we apply the criteria of diction and style we find, on the one hand, that the language is largely free from southern loanwords* and the style wholly untouched by the influences of medieval chivalry and romanticism so evident in Icelandic literature from the middle of the thirteenth century onward; on the other hand, that the style is far superior to that of demonstrably earlier sagas in elegance and incisiveness.

Summing up, we shall not be far wrong in concluding that our saga was composed during the thirties or forties of the thirteenth century.

We can never be grateful enough to the Icelandic scholars of the seventeenth and eighteenth centuries who out of devotion for their native literary inheritance set themselves the task of copying the priceless manuscripts of the Arna-Magnæan collection. But for their selfless efforts, many of the finest sagas would have been irretrievably lost in the great conflagration of 1728 which destroyed the University of Copenhagen library. Thus the best version of the *Eyrbyggja,* which was contained in the manuscript codex of the fourteenth century called *Vatnshyrna,* would have been lost (except for a few leaves) if it were not for the faithful copies made of it, one by Ásgeir Jónsson and the great collector, Árni Magnússon, himself; another by Ketill Jörundarson. Hardly less valuable, but unfortunately lacking all but the middle part of the saga, is a manuscript from the fourteenth century belonging to the Wolfenbüttel library. Besides there exist a number of fragments of a different version. The relation of these manuscripts to one another is set forth in the editions of Vigfússon (1864), Gering (1897), and Sveinsson (1935). The present translation is based on the *Vatnshyrna* version as edited by Gering and Sveinsson. Previous to the present translation, the only one rendering the complete saga in English was the version (in volume II of their Saga Library) by that great poet, William Morris, aided by the Icelandic scholar, Eiríkur Magnússon (1892). It has admirable notes, but because of the unfortunate misconception—not dead yet—that the sagas require an antiquarian language flavored with English dialecticisms, is almost unreadable today.

---

*Though they are more numerous than the latest editor, Einar Ól. Sveinsson, would admit.

CHAPTER 1

Ketil Flatnose makes himself Lord of the Hebrides.

KETIL FLATNOSE WAS THE NAME of a noble lord in Norway. He
was the son of Bjorn Buna, the son of Grím, a lord of Sogn.[1] Ketil was
married. His wife was Yngvild, the daughter of Ketil Wether, a chieftain of Raumaríki.[2] Their sons were called Bjorn and Helgi; and their
daughters were Aud the Profound, Thórunn Hyrna, and Jórunn the
Sagacious. Ketil's son Bjorn was given in fosterage to be reared by
Earl Kjallak of Jamtaland,[3] who was a wise and excellent man. This
earl had a son who was likewise called Bjorn and a daughter named
Gjaflaug.

That was at the time when King Harold Fairhair came to power in
Norway. Because of the hostilities [which ensued] many distinguished
men abandoned their ancestral homes in Norway, some going eastward
across the Keel [Mountains][4] and others westward over the North Sea.
Some of the latter passed the winter in the Hebrides or the Orkney
Islands, but in the summer they went raiding in Norway and caused
great damage in the realm of King Harold. The farmers complained of
this to the king and asked him to rid them of this disturbance. Thereupon King Harold decided to muster a fleet and send it westward over
the North Sea, and he ordered Ketil Flatnose to head that force. Ketil
sought to excuse himself, but the king stood on his going. So when
Ketil saw that the king insisted on having his way, he got himself ready
for the voyage; and he took with him his wife and those of his children
who were at home.

When Ketil came to the western lands, he fought several battles and
was always victorious. He made himself master of the Hebrides. Then
he concluded a peace with the greatest chieftains in the Western Isles

---

[1]District around the Sogn Fjord in West Norway.
[2]The present Romerike, district in southeastern Norway.
[3]Jämtland, a province in western Sweden formerly belonging to Norway. The
practice of having one's children reared by foster parents was common in Scandinavian antiquity.
[4]So named because they form the backbone of the Scandinavian peninsula.

1

and entered into alliances with them; but the fleet he sent back to Norway. And when they came before King Harold, they said that Ketil Flatnose was now the ruler of the Hebrides, but they did not say that they had observed that he was furthering the power of King Harold in those parts. And when the king heard that, he seized all the properties which Ketil owned in Norway. Ketil Flatnose gave his daughter Aud in marriage to Óláf the White, who was at that time the greatest warrior king in the Western Seas. He was the son of Ingjald, the son of Helgi. The mother of Ingjald was Thóra, the daughter of Sigurd Worm-in-the-Eye, the son of Ragnar Lodbrók.[5] He married Thórunn Hyrna to Helgi the Lean, the son of Eyvind the Norwegian and of Rafurta, the daughter of Kjarval, a king over the Irish.

---

[5] The famous legendary hero.

CHAPTER 2

*Bjorn, the son of Ketil, is outlawed by King Harold
and is granted refuge by Thórólf Mostrarskegg.*

BJORN, THE SON OF Ketil Flatnose, remained in Jamtaland until Earl Kjallak died. He married the earl's daughter Gjaflaug and then traveled westward over the Keel, first to Thrándheim,[1] and then southward, and took possession of the estates which had belonged to his father. He drove away the stewards whom the king had placed over them. King Harold was in Vík[2] when he heard about this, and he went by the overland route north to Thrándheim. And when he arrived there, he summoned the Frosta Thing; and at this assembly he banished Bjorn Ketilsson from Norway and decreed that he might be killed or seized with impunity

---

[1] The district around the Trondheim Fjord.
[2] The district around the Oslo Fjord.

wherever he might be found. Thereupon he sent Hauk Hábrók and other warriors of his to kill him if they should find him. And when these rounded Cape Stad[3] on their journey south, Bjorn's friends became aware of them and informed him of their approach. Bjorn with his household and his movable goods then got aboard a small vessel which he owned and sailed southward along the coast, for it was then the severest part of winter, and he did not dare venture out on the high seas.

Bjorn sailed until he came to the island called Mostr,[4] which lies off Sunnhordaland; and there he was well received by a man named Hrólf, the son of Ornólf Fiskreki. There Bjorn remained in hiding during the winter. The king's men turned back after they had confiscated Bjorn's properties and placed men in charge of them.

---

[3]The westernmost promontory of Norway.
[4]Large island at the entrance of the Hardangerfjord in southwestern Norway.

CHAPTER 3

Bjorn is outfitted by Thórólf and sails to the Hebrides.

Hrólf was a powerful chieftain and a man who lived in grand style. He had charge of the temple of Thór there on the island, and was a great friend of Thór, and for that reason was called Thórólf. He was a big, strong man of handsome appearance. Because of his large beard he was called Mostrarskegg.[1] He was the most eminent man on the island.

---

[1]Both the derivation of *Thórólfr* as being from Thór and Hrólfr and the explanation of the cognomen *Mostrarskegg* as a compound of *skegg* 'beard' are interesting popular etymologies. Actually, *Thórólfr* is from *Thórúlfr* ('wolf'); *skegg* secondarily means 'dweller, man'.

In the spring Thórólf gave Bjorn an excellent sea-going vessel and manned it with a good crew. He sent his son Hallstein along with him, and they sailed westward over the sea to look up Bjorn's kinsmen.

But when King Harold learned that Thórólf Mostrarskegg had given shelter to his outlaw Bjorn Ketilsson, he sent his men to him and banished him from the country and ordered him either to leave as an outlaw, like his friend Bjorn, or else to come before the king and put himself completely at his disposition. That was ten years after Ingólf Arnarson had left to settle in Iceland. And that voyage had become very famous, for the men who came back from Iceland said that there were good conditions for settling there.

CHAPTER 4

Thórólf, incurring the wrath of King Harold, sails to Iceland and lands at Thórsness.

THÓRÓLF MOSTRARSKEGG made preparations for a great sacrifice and asked his good friend, the god Thór, to advise him whether he should seek reconciliation with the king or leave the country and seek his fortune elsewhere. And the answer directed Thórólf to Iceland. Thereupon he procured for himself a large sea-going vessel and equipped it for the voyage to Iceland, and he took with him his kinsfolk, his movable goods, and his livestock. Many of his friends went on the same journey with him. He razed the temple and took along most of the wood of which it had been constructed and also some earth from beneath the pedestal on which the image of Thór had stood. Then Thórólf put out to sea with a favorable wind and found the land. He sailed westward along the south coast and around Reykjaness. Then the wind fell, and they saw that the land was indented with large fjords.

Then Thórólf cast overboard the high-seat pillars which had stood in his temple. On one of them was carved a figure of Thór. He declared that he would settle in that place in Iceland where Thór caused the pillars to come ashore.[1] And as soon as they drifted away from the ship, they were carried into the westernmost fjord; and they seemed to move less slowly than one might have expected.[2] After that a sea breeze sprang up; they then sailed westward around Snæfellsness and into the fjord. They saw that this fjord was extremely broad and long, with great mountains on both sides. Thórólf gave a name to the fjord and called it Broad Firth. He landed on the south side of the fjord, near the middle, and brought his ship into the inlet which they afterwards called Hofsvág. After that they explored the land and found that Thór had come ashore with the pillars on a promontory projecting out to sea north of the inlet. That place has since been called Thórsness. Thereupon Thórólf carried fire around his landtake, which extended from the mouth of Stafá Creek inland to the river which he called Thórsá; and he gave land there to those who had come with him.[3]

He built a large farmhouse at Hofsvág and called it Hofstead; there he had a temple erected, and it was a large building.[4] The entrance was in the side wall near the one end. Inside stood the high-seat pillars, and in them were fastened nails. These were called nails of the gods. The whole interior was a place of refuge. Farther in there was a room shaped as the choirs are now in churches. Here on the floor in the middle of the room stood a pedestal like an altar; and on it lay a ring open in one place, twenty ounces in weight, on which all men were to swear their oaths.[5] This ring the temple priest was supposed to wear on his arm at all meetings. On the pedestal also was the place for the sacrificial bowl and in it a sacrificial twig which was like an aspergill. With this they sprinkled the blood from the bowl which was called sacrificial blood, that is, the blood of those animals which were killed as an offering to the gods.

---

[1] The high seat or seat of honor was a bench, large enough for two or three men, placed near the center of the hall or sitting room. It was flanked on both sides by carved pillars.

[2] An indication of their magic power. Sometimes such pillars or other objects on which had been conferred magic powers, as e.g. the bewitched tree trunk in *Grettis saga,* were believed to move against wind or tide.

[3] The frequently mentioned practice of marking the boundaries of a 'landtake' with fire had both a legal and a religious significance. By sanctifying the land with fire one rendered friendly, or subdued, the spirits of the locality.

[4] This farm is still called *Hofsstaðir* ('Temple Stead') today. The authenticity of the temple description has been verified by excavations in this and other localities.

[5] This ring was probably of silver. Rings of a similar description have been unearthed since.

Around the pedestal in this side room were arranged the images of the gods. Everyone was to pay a contribution to the temple, and they also had to accompany the temple priest to all assemblies, just as thingmen now must accompany their chieftains.[6] On his part, the priest (godi) had to maintain the temple at his own expense, so that it did not deteriorate, and hold the sacrificial banquets in it.

Thórólf gave the name Thórsness to the region between the Vigrafjord and Hofsvág.[7] On this ness there stands a mountain. For this mountain Thórólf had such great reverence that no man might look at it without first having washed. Nothing was to be killed on this mountain, neither cattle nor human beings, except those cattle which left there of their own accord. That mountain he called Helgafell; and he believed that he would enter it when he died, and also all his kinsmen on the ness.[8] At the place where Thór had come ashore, on the point of the ness projecting into the sea, he had all the courts held. And there he established the district assembly. This too was such a holy place for him that he would not allow it to be defiled in any way whatsoever, either through bloodshed or through human excrement. For this purpose a skerry was set aside which was called Dirtskerry. Thórólf maintained a magnificent establishment and had a large number of men about him since good supplies of food could be obtained both from the islands and from the sea.[9]

---

[6]The temple priest *(goði, hofgoði)*—the title is difficult to render adequately—had both religious and secular prerogatives. His office was called *goðorð*. The liegemen of his district, who were known as his thingmen, had to pay toll to the temple, of which he was both priest and owner, and render him service on all his expeditions. All disputes within his district were referred to him for settlement.
[7]*Hofsvág* means 'Temple Bight'.
[8]A fairly common belief in pagan times. *Helgafell* means 'Holy Mountain'.
[9]The islands supplied birds, birds' eggs, eider down, and frequently seals in addition to fish.

CHAPTER 5

Bjorn stays with his Christian kinfolks for two years.

Now THIS IS TO BE TOLD about Bjorn, the son of Ketil Flatnose. He sailed westward across the North Sea after he had taken leave of Thórólf Mostrarskegg, as was told before. He set his course for the Hebrides. When he arrived there, however, his father Ketil had already died; but he found there his brother Helgi and his sisters, and they offered him good conditions to live with them. Bjorn learned that they had a different faith, and he considered it paltry of them to have renounced the old faith which their kinsmen had had. He did not feel at home with them, and so did not wish to make his permanent residence there. He spent the winter, however, with his sister Aud and her son Thorstein. But when they found out that he would not agree with his relatives, they called him Bjorn the Norwegian;[1] and they were displeased because he would not settle there.

---

[1]Since *inn austrœni* may mean either 'the Easterner', i.e., 'the Norwegian' or 'renegade, sheep straying from the flock', there is a telling irony in the epithet.

CHAPTER 6

Bjorn sails to Iceland and settles near Thórólf.

BJORN REMAINED IN THE Hebrides for two years before he made ready to sail to Iceland. With him on this voyage was Hallstein Thórólfsson.

They landed in the Broad Firth; and on the advice of Thórólf, Bjorn took land between Stafá Creek and Hraunsfirth. Bjorn settled in Borgarholt in Bjarnarhaven. He was most highly regarded. Hallstein Thórólfsson thought it unmanly to accept land from his father, and so he sailed westward over the Broad Firth and took land there and settled at Hallsteinsness.[1]

Several years later Aud the Profound came out to Iceland. She spent the first winter with her brother Bjorn. Afterwards she took possession of all the land in the Dales District between the rivers Skraumuhlaupsá and Dogurdará and settled at Hvamm. During this time all the lands around the Broad Firth were settled, but there is no need to speak here of the settlements of those men who do not occur in this saga.

---

[1]Actually, north across the Broad Firth, as Hallsteinsness is on the opposite side.

CHAPTER 7

Other settlers. —Thórólf has a son, Thorstein.

GEIRROD WAS THE NAME of a man who took land from the river Thorsá inward as far as Longdale and lived at Eyr.[1] With him came Úlfar the Champion, to whom he gave land around Úlfarsfell, and Finngeir the son of Thorstein Snowshoe, who settled in the Álptafirth District. His son was Thorfinn, the father of Thorbrand of Álptafirth.

Vestar was the name of a man, the son of Thórólf Bladderpate, who came to Iceland with his old father and took land beyond the Urthvalafirth and lived at Ondurd Eyr. His son was Ásgeir, who lived there afterward.

---

[1]This Eyr (meaning 'sandbank' or 'spit'), directly east of the Thórsness Peninsula, is to be distinguished from the farm Ondurd Eyr, which lies some ten miles west of Thórsness and was the home of Ásgeir, mentioned below.

Bjorn the Norwegian was the first of these original settlers to die, and he was buried in a mound near Borgar Creek. He left behind two sons: the first was Kjallak the Old, who dwelled at Bjarnarhaven after the death of his father. Kjallak's wife was Ástríd, the daughter of the chieftain Hrólf, the sister of Steinólf the Short. They had three children. Their son was Thorgrím the godi. One daughter was Gerd, who was married to the godi Thormód, the son of Odd the Bold. The third child was Helga, the wife of Ásgeir of Eyr. From the children of Kjallak are descended numerous kinsfolk who are called the Kjalleklings. Bjorn's other son was named Óttar. He married Gró Geirleifsdóttir, the sister of Oddleif of Bardastrand. Their sons were Helgi, the father of Ósvíf the Wise, and Bjorn, the father of Vigfús of Drápuhlíd. Vilgeir was the name of the third son of Óttar Bjarnarson.

Thórólf Mostrarskegg was married in his old age to a woman named Unn. Some say that she was the daughter of Thorstein the Red, but Ari Thorgilsson the Learned does not include her among his children.[2] Thórólf and Unn had a son who was called Stein. Thórólf dedicated this boy to his friend Thór and named him Thorstein, and this boy was very precocious. Thórólf's son Hallstein married Ósk, the daughter of Thorstein the Red. Their son was also named Thorstein. Thórólf reared him as his foster son and called him Thorstein the Black; his own son, however, he called Thorstein Thorskabít.[3]

---

[2]It is not certain which work of the famous historian Ari is referred to here.
[3]The surname Thorskabít may mean 'one who is eager to catch cod'.

CHAPTER 8

Thórólf Lamefoot acquires land by force.

AT THAT TIME GEIRRÍD, the sister of Geirrod of Eyr, came out to Iceland; and he gave her land in Borgardale in the inner part of the Álptafirth. She had her hall built across the common traveled way, and all were [invited] to ride through it. There was always a table there with food on it, which was given to all who wished to eat. For this reason she was regarded as a most generous woman. Geirríd had been married to Bjorn, the son of Bolverk the Rash;[1] and their son was called Thórólf. He was a great viking. He came out to Iceland somewhat later than his mother and stayed with her during the first winter.

It seemed to Thórólf that there was too little farm land there, and so he challenged Úlfar the Champion to a *hólmgang* for his land since he was advanced in years and childless.[2] Úlfar would rather die than be cowed by Thórólf. They went to an island in the Álptafirth, and Úlfar fell; but Thórólf was wounded in the leg so that he walked with a limp ever after. For this reason he was called Lamefoot. He built a house at Hvamm in Thórsárdale. He took over Úlfar's land and was an extremely unjust and overbearing man. He sold land to two freedmen of Thorbrand of Álptafirth; to Úlfar he sold Úlfarsfell,[3] and to Orlyg, Orlygsstead; and they lived there for a long time afterward.

Thórólf Lamefoot had three children. Arnkel was the name of his son, and Gunnfríd was the name of his daughter who was married to Thorbeinir of Thorbeinisstead on the Vatnsháls Ridge inland from the farm Drápuhlíd. Their sons were Sigmund and Thorgils, and his daughter was Thorgerd, who was married to Vigfús of Drápuhlíd. The other daughter of Thórólf Lamefoot was named Geirríd. She was married to Thórólf, the son of Herjólf Holkinrazi,[4] and they lived at Mávahlíd. Their children were Thórarin the Black and Gudný.

---

[1]The cognomen *Blindingatrjóna* ('gadfly-snout') seems to be a colorful designation for rashness. Other interpretations are possible.

[2]A *hólmgang* ('island going') was a duel, originally fought, as the name indicates, on an island. The circumstance that Úlfar was old and childless was legally important: there were no near relatives to take up the prosecution for manslaughter.

[3]This Úlfar is, of course, not the same person as Úlfar the Champion.

[4]The cognomen probably means 'dweller on stony land'.

CHAPTER 9

Battle over the sacrosanctity of the ground of Thórsness.

WHEN THÓRÓLF MOSTRARSKEGG died at Hofstead, Thorstein Thorskabít inherited the farm from his father. He took as his wife Thóra, the daughter of Óláf Feilan and sister of Thórd Yeller, who was then living at Hvamm. Thórólf was buried in a mound on Haugsness west of Hofstead.

At that time the overbearing of the Kjalleklings was so great that they deemed themselves superior to the other men in that district. Bjorn had so many kinsmen that no other clan in the Broad Firth was so numerous. Barna-Kjallak, one of their kinsmen, was then living in Medalfell Strands at the place which is now called Kjallaksstead. He had many and well-bred sons. They all supported their kinsmen in the south of the fjord at assemblies and meetings.

It happened one spring at the Thórsness Assembly that Thorgrím Kjallaksson and his brother-in-law Ásgeir of Eyr declared they would no longer put up with the arrogance of the Thórsness people. They said, furthermore, that they would ease themselves on the grass there as anywhere else at meetings even though those people were so haughty that they considered their lands more sacred than other farms in Broad Firth. They stated openly that they would not wear out their shoes going to the skerry for their needs. But when Thorstein Thorskabít heard of this, he did not want to stand for it that they should defile the field which his father Thórólf had revered above all other places on his lands. He called his friends to him and decided to keep the others from the field by force if they attempted to defile it. Thorgeir Keng, the son of Geirrod of Eyr, and the Álptafirth people Thorfinn and his son Thorbrand, and Thórólf Lamefoot and many other thingmen and friends of Thorstein agreed to stand by him in this matter.

In the evening when the Kjalleklings had finished their meal, they took their weapons and went out in the direction of Thórsness. And when Thorstein and his followers saw them turn off the path that led to the skerry, they seized their weapons and ran after them with challenging shouts. When the Kjalleklings saw that, they closed their ranks and defended themselves. But the men of Thórsness made such a fierce onslaught that they gave ground and retired to the beach. There they faced their opponents again, and a bitter battle ensued between them. The Kjalleklings were fewer in number but had a select band.

Now two men from the Forest Strand, Thorgest the Old and Áslák from Longdale, caught sight of what was happening. They ran up and went between them, but both parties were fighting so fiercely that the two men were unable to separate them until they declared that they would support that side which was willing to listen to them and break off the fight. Then they quit fighting, although with the condition that the Kjalleklings should not be allowed to go back up to the field. So they boarded their vessel and left the assembly. Some were killed on both sides, but more of the Kjalleklings; and many were wounded. No truce was made since neither party was willing to offer one, but each declared it would attack the other at the first opportunity. The field had become all bloody where they fought as well as where the men of Thórsness had stood during the battle.

CHAPTER 10

Thórd Yeller arranges a composition between the contending parties.

AFTER THIS ASSEMBLY both parties kept a large body of armed men, and there was much suppressed enmity between them. Mutual friends decided to send for Thórd Yeller, who was then the greatest chieftain around the Broad Firth. He was a kinsman of the Kjalleklings and a near relative by marriage of Thorstein. He seemed to be the most likely person to bring about a reconciliation. When Thórd received this message, he set out with a large band of followers to try to make peace. He found that the differences of opinion between them were very great; yet he was able to effect a truce and an appointment for a meeting.

The conclusion of the matter was that Thórd should arbitrate, but with these conditions: the Kjalleklings stipulated that they would never go to the Dirtskerry for their needs, and Thorstein stipulated that the Kjalleklings should not defile the field now any more than before. The Kjalleklings declared that there should be no indemnity for those who had fallen on Thorstein's side since they had set out with the intention of attacking them. The men of Thórsness, however, maintained there should be no compensation for the slain Kjalleklings because of the breach of law committed by them at a hallowed assembly place. But although he knew an adjustment would be difficult to bring about because of the conditions specified, Thórd agreed to make the attempt rather than that they should part unreconciled.

So Thórd made this the first point in his decision, that each should keep the advantage he had gained. He determined that there should be no compensation for the deaths and wounds which had been inflicted on Thórsness. But he declared that the field had been defiled by the bloodshed which had occurred there, so that the ground there was no more sacred than anywhere else, and that they were the cause of it who had started the fight. That by itself, he said, had been a breach of peace. He decided also that assemblies were to be held there no more. But in order that they should henceforth be fully reconciled and on friendly terms, he stipulated that Thorgrím Kjallaksson should have a half share in the maintenance of the temple and receive half the temple dues and also half the thingmen. In return he was henceforth to aid Thorstein in all his lawsuits and support him in maintaining whatever degree of holiness he wished to assign to the place where the assembly was next to be held. Herewith Thórd Yeller gave in marriage to Thorgrím Kjallaksson his kinswoman Thórhild, the daughter of his neighbor Thorkel Meinakr. Because of his new dignity he was called Thorgrím godi.[1]

The place of assembly was then moved farther inland on the promontory to its present site. And when Thórd Yeller created the quarter assemblies, he decided that the assembly of the Western Firths should be held there.[2] Men from all parts of that district were to come there. There is still to be seen there that judgment circle in which men were con-

---

[1] The *goðorð* could be bought and sold, or divided and held in partnership. In the latter case, the sharers in the office all had the right to the title *goði*.

[2] In 964, at the suggestion of Thórd Yeller, four quarter assemblies—for the four quarters of the island—were set up in addition to the various local things and the national assembly (Althing), which had been established in 930.

demned to be sacrificed. In this circle stands the stone of Thór, on which the backs of the men selected for the sacrifice were broken; and the color of blood can still be seen on the stone.[3] This assembly site was extremely sacred, but the men were not forbidden to ease themselves there.

---

[3]To the south of the old assembly site, traces of which can still clearly be seen, stands a blue basaltic stone, partly encrusted by red scoria, which is generally believed to be the stone of Thór. There is, however, no longer any vestige of the circle.

CHAPTER 11

Thorstein drowns and is welcomed into Helgafell Mountain.

THORSTEIN THORSKABÍT lived in grand style. He always had sixty freedmen at his place. He was most active in laying in supplies for the household and was constantly out on the seas fishing. He first had the farmhouse erected at Helgafell and moved his household there, and there was also the greatest temple edifice at that time. Another farm he established there on the promontory near the place where the assembly had formerly been. He had this building elaborately decorated and later gave it to his kinsman Thorstein the Black, and Thorstein lived there afterward and became one of the wisest of men. Thorstein Thorskabít had a son who was called Bork the Stout. And in the summer when Thorstein was twenty-five, Thóra gave birth to a son, whom he named Grím and sprinkled with water. That boy Thorstein dedicated to Thór and declared he should be the temple priest, and so he called him Thorgrím.[1]

In the autumn of that year Thorstein rowed out to the island Hoskuldsey to fish. One evening that autumn Thorstein's shepherd went north of Helgafell to bring in the sheep. He saw the northern slope of the mountain open, and inside he could see great fires, and he could hear

---

[1]The practice of sprinkling a child with water, which is mentioned frequently in the sagas, was a pagan custom.

noisy merriment and the blaring of horns coming from there. And when he listened to hear what was said, he heard Thorstein Thorskabít and his shipmates being welcomed, and Thorstein being invited to sit in the high seat opposite his father.

That same evening the shepherd told Thóra, Thorstein's wife, about this vision. She took it very quietly and said it might be an omen of important events. On the following morning men came in from Hoskulds-ey and brought the news that Thorstein Thorskabít had been drowned while fishing. People deplored his death greatly. Thóra managed the household after that, and a man named Hallvard came to share the man-agement with her. They had a son who was called Már.

CHAPTER 12

Thórdís, Gísli's sister, is married to Bork. Her son, Snorri, is given in fosterage to Thorbrand.

THE SONS OF Thorstein Thorskabít grew up at home with their mother and were very promising men, but Thorgrím excelled the others in every respect, and so he became temple priest as soon as he was old enough.[1] Thorgrím married Thórdís, the daughter of Súr of Dýra Fjord to the west, and lived there in the neighborhood of his brothers-in-law Gísli and Thorkel. Thorgrím killed Véstein Vésteinsson during an autumn feast in Haukadale. But the following fall when Thorgrím was twenty-five (like his father), Gísli, his brother-in-law, killed him at an autumn festival at Sæból.[2] Several days later his wife Thórdís gave birth to a child, and this boy was called Thorgrím after his father.[3]

---

[1] Probably when he reached his majority at the age of sixteen.

[2] All this is told in the *Gísla saga Súrssonar,* one of the most moving of the Icelandic family sagas.

[3] A boy was generally not named for his father unless the father had died before the child was born.

A little later Thórdís was married to Bork the Stout, Thorgrím's brother, and went to live with him at Helgafell. Then her son Thorgrím went to Álptafirth, where he was reared as a foster child at the home of Thorbrand. He was somewhat impudent in his youth and was therefore called Snerrir and after that, Snorri.[4] Thorbrand of Álptafirth was married to Thuríd, the daughter of Thorfinn Sel-Thórisson from Raudamel. These were their children: Thorleif Kimbi, Snorri, Thórodd, Thorfinn, and Thormód. Thorgerd was the name of their daughter. All these [young men] were foster brothers of Snorri Thorgrímsson.

At that time Arnkel, the son of Thórólf Lamefoot, lived at Bólstead near Vadilshead. He was a very large and powerful man, a skilful lawman and very wise; he was a manly sort of person and superior to all others there in the district in popularity and hardihood. He too was a temple priest and had many thingmen.

Thorgrím Kjallaksson lived at Bjarnarhaven, as was mentioned previously; and he and Thórhild had three sons. Brand was the oldest. He lived at Krossness near Brimlár Head. The second was Arngrím, a large, strong man. He was swarthy and had a big nose and coarse features. His hair was reddish-blond, and he early became bald on the forehead above the temples. His eyes were large and fine. He was a very overbearing and unjust man, wherefore he was called Styr.[5] Vermund was the name of the youngest son of Thorgrím Kjallaksson. He was a tall man, slender, and handsome in appearance. He was called Vermund the Slender.

A son of Ásgeir at Eyr was named Thorlák. His wife was Thuríd, the daughter of Audun Stoti of Hraunsfirth. These were their children: Steinthór, Bergthór, Thormód, Thórd Blígr, and Helga. Steinthór was the most outstanding of the children of Thorlák. He was a large, strong man, most skilled in arms, and a man of great prowess. He was usually of a calm disposition. Steinthór is said to have been the third best warrior in Iceland after Helgi Droplaugarson and Vémund Kogur.[6] Thormód was a wise man and quite temperate. Thórd Blígr, on the

---

[4] *Snerrir* means 'unruly person'.—Considering the sedate, unimpulsive behavior of Snorri as a mere stripling of fourteen, we are entitled to doubt this statement. Sobriquets often went from father to son.

[5] The cognomen means 'battle, turmoil'. It was so appropriate that it replaced the given name and was further extended to Víga-Styr 'Slaying-Styr' because of his numerous manslaughters.

[6] Helgi and his brother Grím are the heroes of the *Droplaugarsona saga*. *Kögur* means 'fringe, clothing with fringes'.

other hand, was very rash and hasty of speech. Bergthór was the youngest of them, but a youth of great promise.

CHAPTER 13

Snorri journeys to Norway with his foster brothers and returns with them. —Thórdís attempts to avenge her brother Gísli's death.

SNORRI THORGRÍMSSON was fourteen years old when he went abroad with his foster brothers Thorleif Kimbi and Thórodd. His uncle, Bork the Stout, gave him fifty ounces of pure silver for the voyage abroad. They had a good passage and came to Norway in the autumn. They spent the winter in Rogaland.[1] Snorri stayed with Erling Skjálgsson at Sóli, and Erling was hospitable to him since there had been an old friendship between their ancestors Horda-Kári and Thórólf Mostrar-skegg.[2]

The following summer they returned to Iceland, but were somewhat late in starting. They had rough sailing and made the Hornafjord shortly before winter.[3] But when those from the Broad Firth left the ship, there was a great contrast between the equipment of Snorri and that of Thorleif Kimbi. Thorleif had bought the finest horse he could find, and he also had a magnificent stained saddle. He carried an elaborately ornamented sword and a spear inlaid with gold, a dark blue shield richly gilded, and his clothes were of the finest material. For the purchase of these things he had spent practically all the assets he had taken along. Snorri, on the other hand, wore a black hooded cloak and rode a decent black mare. He had an old-fashioned trough-shaped

---

[1] A district in southwestern Norway.

[2] Earl Erling was the great grandson of Horda-Kári, and Snorri was the great grandson of Thórólf.

[3] On the forbidding southeastern coast of Iceland; from there, they had to ride nearly the whole length of the island to get home.

saddle, and his arms were not much ornamented. Thórodd's equipment was somewhere between these two extremes.

They rode westward past Sída, and then along the path leading to the Borgar Firth, and then farther westward over the mountain path called Flotur ('Flats'), and spent the night in Álptafirth. After that Snorri rode to Helgafell, where he intended to stay for the winter. Bork received him coolly, and people made much fun of his outfit. Bork inferred from the looks of it that he had had bad luck with his money, seeing that all was gone.

It happened one day at the beginning of winter that twelve fully armed men came to Helgafell. Their leader was Eyjólf the Gray, a kinsman of Bork and the son of Thórd Yeller. He lived to the west in Otradale in the Arnafirth. When asked about news, they told of the slaying of Gísli Súrsson and of the men who had perished at his hands before he fell. On hearing this, Bork became very gleeful, and he called upon Thórdís and Snorri to welcome Eyjólf warmly as being the man who had removed so great a disgrace from their kinsmen. Snorri appeared little moved by these tidings, but Thórdís said that it would be a good enough welcome—"if porridge were given the killer of Gísli."[4]

Bork retorted, "It is not my business to prepare the food."

Bork had Eyjólf occupy the high seat and seated his followers on both sides of him. They laid their weapons on the floor. Bork sat next to Eyjólf, and Snorri beside Bork. Thórdís brought in the porridge bowls to the table, and she was also holding the spoons. While she was serving Eyjólf, a spoon fell from her hand. Stooping down for it, she seized Eyjólf's sword; and drawing it quickly, she thrust it up under the table into Eyjólf's thigh. The hilt caught on the table, and yet it was a great wound.

Bork thrust the table away and struck at Thórdís. Snorri shoved Bork with such force that he fell. He put his arm around his mother and set her down beside him and said that she had suffered enough as it was without being beaten. Eyjólf and his followers jumped up, but Bork's men restrained them. The conclusion of the matter was that Bork gave Eyjólf the right to determine the indemnity himself, and paid him a

---

[4]Porridge was a common dish but was not regarded as fitting food for esteemed guests. It must be remembered that the slain Gísli was Thórdís' brother. On the other hand, Bork's brother, who was Thórdís' first husband, had been slain by Gísli.

large sum of money in compensation for the injury.[5] Thereupon Eyjólf rode away. Because of this affair the ill-will between Bork and Snorri increased greatly.

---

[5]Injured persons, especially powerful chieftains, were sometimes given 'self-doom', i.e., the right to determine the amount of indemnity they were to receive for the injuries inflicted upon them.

CHAPTER 14

Snorri acquires the estate of Helgafell.

AT THE SPRING assembly the following year Snorri demanded his patrimony from Bork. Bork replied that he would give him his inheritance— "but I am not willing," he said, "to divide Helgafell. Yet I see that you and I are not suited to live together on one farm, and so I shall buy you out so as to own it myself."

Snorri answered, "It seems no more than fair to me that you should set whatever price you wish on the land and that I should choose which one of us shall purchase it."

Bork thought the proposition over and considered that Snorri would not have enough money to pay for the land if he had to pay immediately. So he set the price for half the land at sixty ounces of silver, but first he excluded from this the islands, for he thought he would get them cheaply once Snorri had settled somewhere else.[1] He stipulated also that the money should be paid immediately and that none of it should be borrowed from others. "So now choose, Snorri," said Bork, "right here on the spot what you want to do."

---

[1]The Helgafell islands were especially valuable both for the excellent grazing and for the wealth of bird life on them. The price of sixty ounces for half the land, however, is unrealistic since this sum at that time represented at most the value of thirty-two milch cows.

Snorri replied, "You now show clearly, kinsman Bork, that you think I am short of money when you set such a low price on the land of Helgafell. But I choose to buy my father's land at that price, so make it over to me and give me your hand on it."

"I won't do that," said Bork, "until every single penny has been paid."

Snorri turned to Thorbrand, his foster father. "Did I not give you a certain purse last fall?"

"Yes, you did," said Thorbrand and drew the purse from under his cloak.

Then the silver was counted and paid for the land down to the last penny, and there were still sixty ounces of silver left in the purse. Bork accepted the money and made over the land to Snorri.

Afterwards Bork said, "You have become more amply stocked with silver, kinsman, than I had thought. I wish now that we cease harboring the ill-will which has been between us, and I shall propose as a special favor to you that we both live here at Helgafell this next half year since you have a shortage of livestock."

Snorri replied, "You can enjoy the benefit of your cattle yourself. Only move out of Helgafell!"

And Snorri had his way. But when Bork was ready to move away from Helgafell, Thórdís stepped forward and named witnesses to the fact that she declared herself divorced from her husband Bork, and gave as grounds the fact that he had struck her; and she declared she would never again endure his blows. Then the property of both was divided, and Snorri assisted his mother since he was her heir. Then Bork was in the position he had intended for another: he received little for the islands. After that Bork moved away from Helgafell to the western end of Medalfell Strands and lived first at Barkarstead between Orrahvál and Tongue. Later he moved to Glerárskóg and lived there until old age.[2]

---

[2] These locations are in the innermost reaches of the Broad Firth, the Hvammsfirth.

CHAPTER 15

Snorri's appearance and character. —Gunnlaug's dealings with Katla and Geirríd.

SNORRI THORGRÍMSSON established himself at Helgafell, and his mother had charge of the household. Már Halvardsson, Snorri's paternal uncle, moved there with many milch cows and took over the management of the farm. Snorri now maintained a splendid establishment and had many people about him.

Snorri was a man of average height and rather slender. He was of handsome appearance, with regular features, a fair complexion, blond hair, and a red beard. He was usually of an even disposition. It was not easy to detect whether he liked or disliked a thing. He was a shrewd man and foreseeing in many things. He was unforgiving and revengeful. To his friends he gave good counsel, but his enemies rather thought they felt the coldheartedness of his counsels. He now had the custody of the temple and was therefore called Snorri godi. He became a great chieftain, but he was rather envied for his prestige since there were many who felt they were not inferior to him as to birth and believed they were better men in regard to strength and proven hardihood.

Bork the Stout and Thórdís Súrsdóttir had a daughter named Thuríd, who at that time was married to Thorbjorn the Stout at Fródá. He was the son of Orm the Slender, who had taken land along Fródá Creek and established a farm there. His first wife had been Thuríd, the daughter of Ásbrand from Kamb on the Breidavík Inlet. This Thuríd was a sister of Bjorn, the Champion of the Breidavík people, who will come into the story later on, and of Arnbjorn the Strong. The sons of Thorbjorn and Thuríd were Ketil the Champion, Gunnlaug, and Hallstein. Thorbjorn was a man of great account, and overbearing toward weaker men.

At that time Geirríd, the daughter of Thórólf Lamefoot, lived with her son Thórarin the Black at Mávahlíd. He was a big, strong man, unprepossessing and of a quiet disposition, ordinarily a man who had himself well in hand. He was called the peacemaker. He was not wealthy;

yet he had a profitable farm. He was so unaggressive that his enemies said he had the disposition of a woman rather than that of a man. He was married and his wife's name was Aud. Gudný was his sister, who was married to Vermund the Slender.

At Holt, west of Mávahlíd, there lived a widow whose name was Katla. She was of handsome appearance, but she wasn't too well liked by people. Odd was the name of her son. He was a big and hardy fellow, a brawler and a big talker, slippery and given to spreading slander. Gunnlaug, the son of Thorbjorn the Stout, was eager to learn. He was often at Mávahlíd where he learned magical lore from Geirríd Thórólfsdóttir, for she was skilled in witchcraft. One day when Gunnlaug was on his way to Mávahlíd, he came to Holt and had a long talk with Katla. She asked him whether he still intended to go to Mávahlíd—"to make love to the old thing."

Gunnlaug said that was not his reason for going there. "But you are not so young yourself either, Katla, to scoff at Geirríd for being old."

Katla replied, "I do not think that we are equal in that regard, but it doesn't matter. You people do not think there is any woman but Geirríd, but she isn't the only woman who knows some things."

Katla's son Odd often went to Mávahlíd with Gunnlaug; and often when they were late getting back, Katla used to invite Gunnlaug to stay with her overnight, but he always went home.

CHAPTER 16

Arnkel, Geirríd's brother, vindicates her.

Now IT HAPPENED one day at the beginning of the winter in which Snorri first established himself at Helgafell that Gunnlaug Thorbjarnarson went to Mávahlíd together with Odd, Katla's son. Gunnlaug and Geirríd had a long talk together that day. And when it had become quite late in the evening, Geirríd said to Gunnlaug, "I wish you would not go home this evening, for 'water witches are about', and 'fair seems many a foul fiend'. And you look to me as if your good luck had run out."

Gunnlaug replied, "No harm will come to me," he said, "for there are the two of us together."

She said, "Little help will you have from Odd, and it will be your own fault if you suffer for it."

Then Gunnlaug and Odd left her place. They walked along till they came to Holt. Katla had already gone to bed. She asked Odd to invite Gunnlaug to stay overnight. He said he had already done so—"but he wants to go on home," he said.

"Then be his fate as he fashions it," she said.

Gunnlaug did not come home that night. There was talk about going out to search for him, but nothing was done about it. During the night when Thorbjorn looked out, he discovered his son Gunnlaug lying unconscious before the door. He was carried in and undressed. He was all black and blue around the shoulders, and the flesh was torn from the bones. He was confined to his bed all winter because of his injuries, and there was much talk about his ailment. Odd spread the rumor that Geirríd probably had ridden him and said that Gunnlaug and Geirríd had parted in a huff that evening. And most people gave credence to that.

The following spring at the time legally set for summoning, Thorbjorn rode to Mávahlíd and gave notice of his accusation of Geirríd's being a night hag and having caused Gunnlaug's injuries.[1] The case came before the Thórsness Assembly, and Snorri godi supported his brother-in-law Thorbjorn. Arnkel godi, on his part, defended the case for his sister Geirríd. A jury of twelve was selected to render the decision. But neither Snorri nor Arnkel was deemed eligible to render the verdict because of their close relationship to the plaintiff and the defendant.[2] Therefore Helgi Hofgardsgodi, the father of Bjorn, the father of Gest, the father of Skáld-Ref, was called on to render the verdict of the jury of twelve neighbors. Arnkel godi went before the court and swore an oath on the altar ring that Geirríd had not been responsible for the injuries of Gunnlaug. Thórarin and ten other men took the oath with

---

[1]The plaintiff usually summoned the defendant in person at the home of the latter. This citation could not take place earlier than two weeks before a spring assembly or four weeks before the Althing.

[2]The godi supporting the defendant selected the jury, presided in its deliberations, and announced its verdict.

him. And after that Helgi announced a verdict of acquittal. The case
of Snorri and Thorbjorn came to naught, and they lost much standing
thereby.

CHAPTER 17

The battle between the Kjalleklings and Illugi the Black.

AT THIS ASSEMBLY Thorgrím Kjallaksson and his sons contended with
Illugi the Black concerning the marriage settlement and dowry of Illugi's
wife Ingibjorg, the daughter of Ásbjorn, which Tin-Forni had had
in his custody. During the time of the assembly there were great storms,
so that no one could come to the assembly from Medalfell Strands. It
was a great handicap to Thorgrím that his kinsmen were unable to come
there. Illugi had a picked band of 120 men, and he pushed his case hard;
but the Kjalleklings went to the court and wanted to break up the
proceedings. There was much jostling, and men intervened to part
them. The upshot was that Tin-Forni had to pay out the money in accord with Illugi's claim. So says Odd the Skáld in his *drápa*[1] about
Illugi:

1. Great was the throng on Thórsness
   Thing, when that the bold-minded,
   fortune-favored warrior[2]

---

[1]A *drápa* is a longer laudatory poem.

With few exceptions, all stanzas in this saga are in the so-called *dróttkvætt*
(court) measure. For a characterization of this verse form and skaldic style see
Lee M. Hollander's *The Skalds,* Princeton University Press 1945.

[2]Illugi.

Fáfnir's-hoard[3] demanded.
Sithen took that treasure—
truce was hard to come by—
from the hands of Forni
the feeder-of-greedy-ravens.[4]

Later on, the storm abated, and the Kjalleklings arrived from the Strands to the west. Then Thorgrím Kjallaksson would not hold to the agreement and made an attack upon Illugi and his men, and a fight began between them. Snorri godi summoned men to part them, and thereafter a truce was brought about. Three of the Kjallekling people and four of Illugi's men had fallen there. Styr Thorgrímsson slew two men. Thus said Odd in his *drápa* about Illugi:

2. Clearly, buckler-bearers
   broke the faith they had given:
   fell there three of foemen
   before the keen sword-wielder;
   ere that, sagely, Snorri
   settled—famous grew this
   lord's leadership then 'mong
   land-holders—their quarrel.

Illugi thanked Snorri for his aid and offered him money for it, but Snorri said he did not want any reward for his help the first time. Thereupon Illugi invited him to come home with him, and that Snorri accepted, and he then received good gifts. Snorri and Illugi continued to be friends for a while.

---

[3]The dragon Fáfnir brooded on the gold of the Niflungs; hence, Fáfnir's-hoard is a kenning for 'treasure'.
[4]Kenning for 'warrior'.

CHAPTER 18

*Thorbjorn accuses Thórarin of the theft of his horses. They fight,
and Thorbjorn is slain.*

THAT SUMMER Thorgrím Kjallaksson died; and his son, Vermund the
Slender, took over the farm at Bjarnarhaven. He was a wise man and
gave very wholesome advice. Styr had then also been living for some
time at the farm below Hraun a little ways inland from Bjarnarhaven.
He was a shrewd and hardy man. His wife was Thorbjorg, the daughter
of Thorstein Stormnose. Thorstein and Hall were their sons. Ásdís was
the name of their daughter, a spirited and rather proudminded woman.
Styr was a powerful man in his district and kept many followers about
him. He had many enemies, for he committed many manslaughters
but never atoned for them.

That summer a ship came from Norway and anchored in Salteyrarós
Inlet. Half of the ship belonged to Norwegians. Their skipper was
called Bjorn. He took winter lodging with Steinthór at Eyr. The other
half of the ship belonged to men from the Hebrides, and their leader
was named Álfgeir. He went to stay with Thórarin the Black at Mávahlíd, and with him went a man named Nagli, a large swiftfooted fellow.
He was a Scot by extraction.

Thórarin owned a good fighting stallion which he kept up on the
mountain pastures. Thorbjorn the Stout also had many stud-horses,
which he let graze in the mountain meadows and from which he selected one or more horses for fall slaughtering. Now that fall it so
happened that Thorbjorn's horses could not be found although they
were searched for far and wide. The weather was rather severe that
fall.

At the beginning of winter Thorbjorn sent Odd, the son of Katla,
south over the mountains to a place called Hraun. Here lived a man
named Spá-Gils. He was second-sighted and a clever fellow at ferreting
out thefts or other matters which he had a mind to find out.[1] Odd asked
whether it was foreigners, or men from another district, or neighbors
of Thorbjorn who had stolen his horses.

---

[1]The first element in the name Spá-Gils means 'divination, soothsaying'.

Spá-Gils answered, "Tell Thorbjorn exactly what I tell you. I think that his horses probably have not gone far from their pastures, and that it is risky to make accusations, and better to suffer a loss than to stir up great trouble."

But when Odd returned to Fródá, it seemed to Thorbjorn and his followers that the words of Spá-Gils were a sly allusion to the Mávahlíd people. Odd also added that Spá-Gils had implied that those persons were most likely to steal horses who themselves were short of cattle and yet had increased their household beyond the usual number. These words Thorbjorn regarded as directed against the people at Mávahlíd.

Thereupon Thorbjorn left Fródá farm with eleven men. His son Hallstein went along; but Ketil the Champion, his other son, was abroad at that time. In the group was also Thorbjorn's neighbor Thórir, a most vigorous man, who was the son of Orn from Arnarhvál. Odd, the son of Katla, rode with them too. When they came to the home of Katla at Holt, Katla dressed her son in a dark brown kirtle which she had just made. After that they traveled on to Mávahlíd, and there Thórarin and the members of his household were standing in the doorway and saw the men coming. They greeted Thorbjorn and asked what was the news.

Then Thorbjorn spoke. "Our purpose in coming here, Thórarin," he said, "is to look for the horses which were stolen from me in the fall. We want permission to search your place."

Thórarin replied, "Is this search taken up according to law? Have you summoned any legal eyewitnesses to inquire into this case? Will you grant us safety during this search? Have you gone anywhere else to search?"[2]

Thorbjorn answered, "We do not think that it will be necessary to conduct a search elsewhere."

Thórarin replied, "In that case we will flatly refuse permission for this search if you mean to initiate and conduct it in illegal fashion."

Thorbjorn declared, "If you do so, we shall consider it true that you are guilty in this matter, seeing that you do not wish to clear yourself of the charge through the search."

"You may do as you please about that," said Thórarin.

Thereupon Thorbjorn named six men to constitute a door court. He then formally accused Thórarin of the theft of the horses.

---

[2]The purpose of the questions asked by Thórarin was to guarantee that the search through his premises be carried out legally and without danger to his household.

At that moment Geirríd came to the door; and when she saw what was happening, she said, "What people say about you is all too true, Thórarin, that you have a woman's nature rather than a man's if you let Thorbjorn the Stout heap all kinds of insults on you; and I don't know why I have such a son."

Then Álfgeir, the ship's captain, said, "We will back you up for all we are worth, whatever you decide to do."

Thórarin replied, "Nor shall I stand here any longer."

And with that Thórarin and his men rushed out to break up the court. There were seven of them in all, and a fight began immediately. Thórarin killed a servant of Thorbjorn, and Álfgeir another one. There fell also a servant of Thórarin. But no weapon could wound Odd. Aud, the mistress of the house, called to the women to separate them; and they cast clothes over their weapons. After that Thórarin and his men went inside, while Thorbjorn and his followers rode away, declaring they would refer their case to the Thórsness Assembly. They rode up along the inlet and bandaged their wounds near a fenced-off haystack which is called Korngard.

In the homefield at Mávahlíd a hand was found at the place where the fighting had occurred, and it was shown to Thórarin. He saw that it was a woman's hand. He asked where Aud was. He was told that she was lying in her bed. Then he went to her and asked if she was hurt. Aud asked him not to be concerned about that, but he made certain that one of her hands had been cut off. He then called his mother and asked her to bandage her wound.

Then Thórarin and his followers ran out of the house and after Thorbjorn and his men. And when they were a short distance from the fence, they heard them chatting together and how Hallstein said, "Today Thórarin cleared himself of the reproach of cowardice."

"Yes, he fought bravely," said Thorbjorn, "but many a man does so when he is in a tight spot even though he may not be so courageous otherwise."

Odd said, "Thórarin may be a great fighter, but it will be considered a bad mishap that he cut off his own wife's hand."

"Is that true?" asked Thorbjorn.

"True as day," replied Odd.

Then they sprang to their feet and raised a big scornful laughter at this. Right then Thórarin and his band were upon them, with Nagli at their head. But when he saw them brandishing their weapons, he became terrified and dashed past them and up the mountain, out of his mind with fear. Thórarin ran at Thorbjorn and struck him in the head with his sword and cleft it down to his jaw teeth. Thereupon Thórir Arnarson with two others set on Thórarin, and Hallstein and another attacked Álfgeir. Odd and one other man made for one of Álfgeir's men, and three of Thorbjorn's fellows fought two of Thórarin's men. It was the fiercest encounter, and the outcome was that Thórarin cut off Thórir's leg where the calf is thickest and slew both of his companions. Hallstein fell gravely wounded before Álfgeir. But when Thórarin had disengaged himself, Odd with two others took to flight. He was not wounded, for no weapon could pierce his kirtle. All the other men of Thorbjorn's party lay dead, and both of Thórarin's servants were slain.

Thórarin and his men took the horses of Thorbjorn and his followers and rode them home. They saw Nagli running high up along the hillside. And when they had arrived at the homefield, they saw that Nagli had gotten past the outer fence and was headed for the Búland Promontory. There he came upon two of Thórarin's slaves, who were driving sheep down from the headland. He told them about the encounter between Thórarin and Thorbjorn and what the odds were, and he said he knew for certain that Thórarin and his men were dead; and just then they saw men riding from the farmhouse across the field.

Then Thórarin and his men hastened their pace, for they wished to help Nagli and prevent him from leaping into the sea or down from the cliffs. But when Nagli and the other two saw the men riding so swiftly, they thought it must be Thorbjorn pursuing them. They again took to their heels and ran up the headland and then on to the spot which is now called Thrælaskrida.[3] There Thórarin and his men overtook Nagli, for he was nearly dead from overexertion. But the slaves leaped down from the headland and perished, as could not be otherwise, for the headland is so high that a fall from there means certain death. Thereupon Thórarin and his men returned to the house. Geirríd stood in the doorway and asked what turn things had taken. Then Thórarin spoke this verse:

3. Women's contemptuous taunts I
    turned from me—dun eagles
    fed there on the flesh of
    foemen—as I battled.
    Little spared I, strife-loving

---

[3]'Thralls' Landslide'.

lady,[4] to wield ruthlessly—
loath though to boast—my bitter
brand in mortal conflict.

Geirríd asked, "Are you telling me that Thorbjorn is slain?"
Thórarin spoke this verse:

4. Keen-edged, my cutting broadsword—
    quenched was the blood nowise—
    cleft his shoulder-crag,[5] though
    covered, down through the middle:
    down flowed the dew-of-wounds[6]—his
    deadly sword did graze me—
    over his ears, and swiftly
    entered the warrior's gullet.

"Then my egging you on did some good," exclaimed Geirríd. "Now
all go inside and bind up your wounds." They did so.

Now to tell about Odd. He continued on until he came to Fródá, and
there he told what had happened. Housewife Thuríd had men summoned to fetch the dead and to bring home the wounded. Thorbjorn
was laid in a burial mound, but his son Hallstein was healed. Thórir
of Arnarhvál also recovered, but he had to walk with a wooden leg
ever after. For this reason he was called Thórir Woodenleg. His wife
was Thorgríma Galdrakin. Their sons were Orn and Valr, both doughty
men.

---

[4] I.e., his mother, Geirríd.
[5] Kenning for 'head'.
[6] Kenning for 'blood'.

CHAPTER 19

Thórarin seeks the support of Vermund and Arnkel.

THÓRARIN SPENT THE NIGHT at home at Mávahlíd. And in the morning Aud asked him what he planned to do.

"I would not like to turn you out of house and home," she said, "but I am afraid that more than one door court will be held here this winter; because I am sure that Snorri godi will intend to take up the prosecution for his brother-in-law Thorbjorn."

Then Thórarin spoke this verse:

5. Would not the wise lawyer[1]
   this winter make me outlaw—
   there lies, methinks, my hope, and
   thanks then would I owe him,
   if that, woman, I could
   only the help come by—
   feasters-on-the-fallen[2]
   fed I—of trusty Vermund.

Then Geirríd said, "The most advisable thing to do now is to seek help from such kinsmen-in-law as Vermund or my brother Arnkel."

Thórarin replied, "More than likely we will need both of them before this matter is settled. But first I shall see what help I can get from Vermund."

The same day all who had had a part in the encounter rode to Bjarnarhaven, skirting the firths, and arrived there in the evening. They entered just as the men were sitting down [for their evening meal]. Vermund made them welcome and at once made room for Thórarin and his men on the seat of honor. And when they had taken their places, Vermund asked what news they had.

Thórarin spoke a verse:

---

[1]Viz., Snorri godi.
[2]Kenning for 'ravens, eagles'.

6. Of hard fight—let the host now
   hearken—can I tell you
   fully—I warn the warriors
   beware of shower-of-arrows[3]—
   how the heavy-handed
   helmet-bearers—saw I
   at wrist Aud's right hand severed—
   wrongfully attacked me.

"What can you tell us about that, kinsman?" asked Vermund.
Thórarin spoke this verse:

7. Beset me the sword-wielder,
   seeking to put me in danger,
   but my brand, forth flashing,
   bit him in the skirmish;
   the speeder-of-spears[4] we
   spared but little, although
   rarely fell I foul of
   foe, once the quarrel was ended.

His sister Gudný stopped [before the men on the high seat] and said,
"I suppose you have cleared yourself of the taunts of the people out west
there?"
Thórarin spoke this verse:

8. Was I bound to ward off—
   warm blood dripped from spear-points,
   shields were shivered in combat—
   shame of being a coward,
   when that 'gainst my helmet
   whined his shield-destroyer[5]
   harmless—clashed the halberds,
   hot gushed streams of wound-gore.[6]

Vermund said, "It would seem you had a fierce fight."
Thórarin spoke this verse:

---

[3]Kenning for 'battle': he warns them of battles to come.
[4]Kenning for 'warrior'.
[5]Kenning for 'sword'.
[6]Kenning for 'blood'.

9. Sang there the death-dealing
   dire swift arrows, shot by
   abettors-of-grim-battles,[7]
   buzzing 'gainst my buckler,
   When the dew-of-wounds darkling
   drenched the sun-of-the-gunwales[8]—
   waxed the din of weapons,
   war-cry wild—as we fought there.

Vermund asked, "I wonder if they know now whether you are a man
or a woman?"
Thórarin spoke this verse:

10. I turned from me the taunts—and
    triumphed over Thorbjorn—
    of being a coward, back on
    bold steerer-of-seasteeds,[9]
    whatever Hild's-weapons'-
    haughty-wielder[10]—ravens
    fed upon the fallen
    foe—may tell his leman.

After that Thórarin told them what had happened.
Then Vermund asked, "Why did you pursue them? Did you think
you had not done enough the first time?"
Thórarin spoke this verse:

11. Said it may be, sword-blade-
    swinger—wolves I never
    stinted steaming blood—that
    stung I was to the quick, when
    mainsworn men had twitted
    me, peace-loving, I had
    hewn the hand of my own
    Hlín[11]-of-velvet, bungling.

---

[7]Kenning for 'warriors'.
[8]Kenning for 'shields'. The (round) shields were fastened to the gunwale of
the viking ships for added protection.
[9]Kenning for 'steersman, warrior'.
[10]Hild is a valkyrie; the whole, a kenning for 'warrior'.
[11]A goddess; the whole, a kenning for 'woman, wife'.

"You are certainly justified for not enduring that taunt! How did the foreign men conduct themselves?"

Thórarin spoke this verse:

12. Few of famished ravens
    fed were there by Nagli:
    ready was he rather to
    run up to the mountains.
    Dashed though, helmet-dight, to
    din-of-battle Álfgeir,
    fearless—his flame-of-combat[12]
    flashed out 'gainst the enemy.

"So Nagli didn't bear himself well?" asked Vermund.

Thórarin spoke this verse:

13. Weeping, the wight ran from
    war-play, the bold fighter,[13]
    nor had the doughty hero[13]
    hopes to save his skin whole;
    the minder-of-mares,[14] quite
    mad with fear—forsooth the
    ale-bearer[14] was addled—
    almost leaped o'er the sea-cliff.

And when Thórarin had been at Bjarnarhaven for the night, Vermund said, "You may think that I am not behaving very handsomely about supporting you. But I do not dare offer you shelter unless more men join us in this difficult situation. Let us ride to Bólstead today to see your kinsman Arnkel and find out what he will do about backing us up, because I believe Snorri godi will bear down heavily in seeking retribution."

"I shall let you decide about that," said Thórarin.

And when they were starting out, Thórarin spoke this verse:

14. At ease, thou oak-of-combat[15]—
    ere that I slew the warrior—
    nor threatened we thought us:

---

[12]Kenning for 'sword'.
[13]Ironic, of course.
[14]Kenning for 'menial'.
[15]Kenning for 'warrior'.

that we shall oft remember.
This fear I now, fairest
flax-goddess,[16] that we shall
be the butt—I loathe all
bloody fray—of Snorri.

In this verse he referred to Snorri godi. Vermund and Thórarin rode to Bólstead, and Arnkel welcomed them and asked the news. Thórarin spoke this verse:

15. Odious, armring-giver,
    even to think—did bloody
    swords dissever limbs—of
    slaughter at my farm-yard
    when, thrown in thing-of-weapons[17]
    through the moon-of-gunwales,[18]
    murderous spears dismembered
    many a tree-of-combat.[19]

Arnkel asked just what had happened; and when Thórarin had told him, Arnkel said, "You certainly were aroused to rage, kinsman, you who otherwise are so gentle."
Thórarin spoke this verse:

16. Goaded me the guardians-of-
    gold—me, the peace-loving,
    who had always held his
    hates in leash—to do this:
    often awful downpour
    after calm day cometh.[20]
    Let the lively flax-Gerth[21]
    learn what I have spoken.

"That may well be," said Arnkel. "But I wish to ask you, kinsman Thórarin, to remain here with me until your case is concluded in one

---

[16]Kenning for 'woman'.
[17]Kenning for 'battle'.
[18]See note 8 on stanza 9.
[19]Kenning for 'warrior'.
[20]An allusion to the sudden rage of Thórarin.
[21]A goddess; the whole, a kenning for 'woman'. The reference here, as in the next stanza, is to Thorbjorn's lighthearted wife Thuríd, Snorri's half-sister.

way or another. And, Vermund, I want to ask you not to withdraw from this lawsuit even though I have taken the initiative and have invited Thórarin to stay here."

"It is only my duty," said Vermund, "to aid Thórarin as much as I can. Nor will it make any difference that you take the leadership in helping him."

Then Arnkel said, "I suggest that we stick close together during the winter since Snorri godi is so near."

They did that and arranged it so that Arnkel had a large number of followers at his place during the winter. Vermund stayed alternately in Bjarnarhaven and with Arnkel. Thórarin was reserved for the most part, and his disposition remained unchanged. Arnkel was a very hospitable and cheerful man, and he did not like it if others were not equally cheerful. He often admonished Thórarin to be unconcerned and of good cheer. He said that the widow at Fródá[22] had easily gotten over her grief—"and she would consider it a good joke if you did not bear yourself manfully."

Thórarin spoke this verse:

> 17. Nowise need the tipsy
>   nimble-footed one poke
>   fun at me—on the fallen
>   fed I have the ravens—
>   that I abide not bloodshed—
>   bitter strife has arisen:
>   hungry hawks-of-corpses[23]
>   hie them hither—in battle.

To this, one of Arnkel's manservants replied, "You won't know before spring, at the end of the Thórsness Assembly, how much you can depend on yourself alone in this business."

Thórarin spoke this verse:

> 18. Face we would our fill of
>   feuds, thus say the people—
>   for counsel let us look toward
>   leader who wields power—
>   barring Arnkel back us—

---

[22]I.e., Thurid.
[23]Kenning for 'ravens'.

bright will ring the praises
of hardy helmet-bearer—
helpfully in this matter.

CHAPTER 20

Arnkel puts Katla and Odd to death.

GEIRRÍD, THE MISTRESS of the household at Mávahlíd, sent word to Bólstead that she had learned for certain that Odd, the son of Katla, was the one who had cut off Aud's hand. She declared that Aud had told her this herself, and also that Odd had bragged about it to his friends. When Thórarin and Arnkel heard that, they set out from Arnkel's place with ten men and rode to Mávahlíd, where they stayed overnight. The following morning they rode to Holt, from where their approach was observed. Odd was the only man there. Katla was sitting on the cross dais[1] of the hall spinning yarn. She told Odd to sit beside her—"and don't move or make a sound." She told the women to remain sitting where they were—"and be quiet," she said. "Let me do the talking."

As soon as Arnkel and his men arrived, they went inside. When they entered the room, Katla greeted Arnkel and asked the news. Arnkel declared he had none and asked where Odd was. Katla said that he had gone south to Breidavík—"and he certainly would not try to avoid meeting you if he were at home, for we have complete confidence in your high-mindedness."

"That may be," said Arnkel, "but we mean to search the premises."

"Do as you like," said Katla, and she told the housekeeper to carry

---

[1]The dais or cross dais was a raised floor along the gable wall of the sitting room or hall.

a light for them and to unlock the storehouse—"for that is the only place
on the farm that is locked."

They saw that Katla was spinning yarn on her distaff. They looked
throughout the house, but they did not find Odd. After that they rode
away.

And when they had come a short distance from the farmstead, Arnkel
stopped and said, "I wonder if Katla pulled the wool over our eyes?
Could that not have been her son Odd which looked to us like a distaff?"

"It is not at all unlikely that she did," replied Thórarin. "Let us go
back."

They did so. And when the people at Holt saw them returning,
Katla said to the women, "You stay in your places again. Odd and
I shall go out to meet them."

But when Odd and Katla left the room, she took Odd to the vestibule
opposite the outer door and began to comb him and to cut his hair.
Arnkel and his men rushed in through the outer door and found Katla
there busying herself with her goat. She was trimming his forelock and
beard and combing his matted pelt. Arnkel and his men entered the
room, but they did not see Odd anywhere. Katla's distaff lay on the
bench. Then they felt sure that Odd had not been there. Then they left
and rode away. But when they approached the spot where they had
turned back the first time, Arnkel said, "Don't you think that it might
have been Odd in the shape of a goat?"

"There is no way of knowing," replied Thórarin, "but if we turn back
now, we ought to lay hands on Katla."

"Let's try once more," said Arnkel, "and see how it turns out." And
so they went back once more.

But when they were seen approaching, Katla told Odd to come with
her. When they had come outside, she went to the ashpile and told
Odd to lie down by it—"and stay there no matter what happens."

When Arnkel and his men arrived at the farmstead, they rushed into
the house and into the room. There sat Katla on the dais spinning.
She greeted them and said that they were paying her frequent visits.
Arnkel said that that was true. His companions seized the distaff and
chopped it to pieces.

Katla said, "Now you won't have to say, when you come home this
evening, that you didn't accomplish anything here at Holt since you
have chopped up my distaff."

Then Arnkel and his men searched for Odd inside and out, but they
saw no living thing except a home-fed boar of Katla's which was lying

by the ashpile. And so they rode away. When they had gone halfway to Mávahlíd, Geirríd came to meet them, and one of her workmen with her. She asked how matters had gone with them. Thórarin told her. She said they had not searched properly for Odd—"and I want you to turn back once more, and I shall go with you. One cannot use halfway measures where Katla is concerned."

Thereupon they turned back. Geirríd had on a blue cloak.[2] And when they were seen approaching by the people at Holt, Katla was told that now there were fourteen in all, one of whom was wearing colored clothing.

Then Katla said, "Then that is Geirríd, the witch, so now mere tricks of magic alone won't do."

She got up from the dais and lifted up a cushion on which she had been sitting. Underneath was a trapdoor and a hollow space inside the dais. She had Odd get in there, and then she arranged everything as it had been before and sat down. She said she felt rather strange.[3]

When Arnkel and his followers entered the room this time, there were no greetings. Geirríd cast her cloak from her and went up to Katla. She took a bag of sealskin which she had brought along and pulled it over her head.[4] Her companions tied it below. Then Geirríd told them to break open the dais. Odd was found there and bound. After that the two were taken to the Búland Promontory, and Odd was hanged there. And as Odd was kicking the gallows, Arnkel said to him, "It's ill hap befalls you through your mother, and it is an evil mother you have, I think."

Katla said, "True it may be that he does not have a good mother, but ill does not befall him because I willed it. But this would be my wish, that ill befall you all from me, and I am thinking that this will come true. And now I shall not conceal from you that it was I who was to be blamed for Gunnlaug Thorbjarnarson's injuries that were the beginning of all this trouble. No ill can befall you, Arnkel, from your mother, since she is no longer living; but that spell would I work on you that worse ill may befall you from your father than has come to Odd from me, and all the more so since you have more at stake than he. And also, I expect that before the end comes, people will say that you had an evil father."

---

[2] Ordinary clothes were of undyed homespun.
[3] Because she feels the influence of the approaching Geirríd.
[4] In order to prevent Katla from putting the "evil eye" on them.

After that they stoned Katla to death there below the headland.[5] Then they rode to Mávahlíd, and remained there for the night, and continued on home the following day. The news of all these events was spread abroad, and no one felt sorry for the two. Thus the winter passed.

---

[5]Similar stories of witchcraft and also of the short shrift given the perpetrators are frequent in the sagas. Note that, having the magic power of the words of a dying person, Katla's curse and prediction are eventually fulfilled.

CHAPTER 21

Arnkel advises Thórarin to leave the country.

ONE DAY the following spring Arnkel called his kinsmen Thórarin and Vermund, and also Álfgeir, for a conference and asked them what sort of aid seemed to them to be of greatest service to Thórarin—whether they should ride to the assembly—"and there try to enlist the help of all our friends. Then one of two things may happen: either that a composition can be brought about, in which case it will come mighty high for you to make atonement for all the men who were slain in your fight or received wounds.[1] It may also happen, if we put in our appearance at the assembly, that our difficulties may grow worse, in case our defense is pushed too vigorously.[2] Another way out," he said, "would be to make every effort to help you to leave the country with your movable goods and trust to luck about such lands of yours as cannot be sold beforehand."

Álfgeir was all in favor of the latter plan. And Thórarin, too, said that he did not have sufficient means to pay the atonement for all the deeds which had been committed in this affair. Vermund declared he would not part from Thórarin, whether he preferred to have him go

---

[1]I.e., for Thórarin and Álfgeir.
[2]Viz., that this might result in another battle.

abroad with him or back him in any fight in this country. But Thórarin chose to have Arnkel help them to leave the country. Thereupon a messenger was sent to Eyr with instructions that skipper Bjorn should do his very best to get their ship ready as soon as possible.

CHAPTER 22

Thórarin and Vermund sail for Norway.

Now TO TELL ABOUT Snorri godi: he took upon himself the prosecution of the cases against the slayers of his brother-in-law Thorbjorn. He also had his sister Thuríd come home to Helgafell because the rumor was being spread about that Bjorn, the son of Ásbrand from Kamb, was having trysts with Thuríd and was seducing her. Snorri believed he could see through the plans of Arnkel and the others as soon as he learned that their ship was being got ready. He assumed they did not intend to pay any compensation for the slayings since they had made no offers of reconciliation. Nevertheless, things remained quiet until the days of summoning. But when this time came, Snorri gathered his followers and rode to Bólstead with eighty men; for at that time the law required that the summons for manslaughter be made at the home or in the hearing of the slayers and that the neighbors should not be summoned as witnesses until the time of the assembly.[1] And when Snorri and his band were seen approaching Bólstead, the men considered whether they should forthwith attack them, for there were a great many followers present. Arnkel said that that should not be— "and Snorri shall have the benefit of the law." He said that with matters as they were, he would do only what necessity demanded.

---

[1]Here our saga reflects older legal procedures. According to Old Icelandic law the neighbors were summoned at their homes, but the charges did not have to be specified before the assembly convened.

When Snorri arrived, there were no provocations from either side. Snorri summoned Thórarin to the Thórsness Assembly as well as all others who had taken part in the fight. Arnkel quietly listened to the summons. After that Snorri and his men left and went up to Úlfarsfell; and when they had ridden away, Thórarin spoke a verse:

19. It is not for ill-doing
     if, lady, the hurlers-
     of-slender-snakes-of-combat[2]
     snatch my freedom from me,
     even though oaken-bucklers'-
     enemies[3]—may gods aid us:
     stronger far the force that
     faces us—make me outlaw.

Snorri godi rode up over the ridge to the farm Hrísar and then on to Drápuhlíd. The following morning he continued on to Swine Lake, and then to Hraunsfirth, and from there the usual way to Trolls' Ridge, and did not stop until he got to the Salteyrarós Inlet. And when they arrived there, some of them pinned down the Norwegians and the others burned the ship; and after having done all that, Snorri and his followers rode home.

Arnkel learned that Snorri had burned the ship. Then Vermund and Thórarin with several men took a boat and rowed westward over the fjord to Dogurdarness,[4] where a ship belonging to some Norwegians was drawn up ashore. Arnkel and Vermund bought the ship; and Arnkel gave Thórarin his half of the ship, while Vermund took care of his share. They moved the ship out to the island Dímun and made it ready there. Arnkel guarded the ship until they were ready to leave, and then sailed with them out past the island of Ellidaey, where they parted as friends. Thórarin and Vermund put out to sea while Arnkel rode home to his farm. Arnkel's conduct won him high praise, and his support of Thórarin was considered most commendable. Snorri godi went to the Thórsness Assembly, where he pursued and won his case. Thórarin and all those who had participated in the fight were declared outlawed; and after the assembly was over, Snorri appropriated all the goods of those outlawed that fell to his share. And that was the end of the action.

---

[2]Kenning for 'spears'.
[3]Kenning for 'warriors'.
[4]Actually, due north.

CHAPTER 23

The encounter between Már and Vigfús' kinsman, Bjorn.

VIGFÚS, THE SON OF Bjorn Óttarsson, was living at Drápuhlíd, as has already been mentioned. His wife was Thorgerd, the daughter of Thorbeinir. He was an excellent farmer, but a very overbearing man. His sister's son Bjorn was staying with him at that time, a loose talker and self-willed fellow.

In the autumn following the suit against Thórarin of Mávahlíd, the breeding horses of Thorbjorn the Stout were found up in the mountains. His stallion had not been able to hold the pastures against the stallion of Thórarin, and the horses had been snowed under, and all were found dead.

That same autumn many men were busy sorting out sheep on the point of land between the two Laxá rivers south of Helgafell. Some of Snorri godi's servants went there to help gather and sort the sheep. Their foreman was Snorri's uncle, Már Hallvardsson. Helgi was the name of his shepherd. Bjorn, Vigfús' kinsman, lay on the wall of the public sheep pen with a mountain staff in his hand. Helgi was sorting out the sheep. Bjorn asked what sheep that was which he was taking. And when they examined the sheep, they saw Vigfús' earmark on it.

Bjorn said, "You're slipshod about sorting the sheep today, Helgi!"

"That's more likely to be the case with you people," retorted Helgi, "who live right close to the common pasture."

"What does a thief like you know about that?" cried Bjorn.

He jumped up and struck him with his staff so that he fell down unconscious. And when Már saw that, he drew his sword and slashed at Bjorn. The blow caught him on the arm near the shoulder and inflicted a great wound. Thereupon the men gathered in two groups, but some others went in between and separated them so that nothing of great moment happened there. On the following morning Vigfús rode down to Helgafell to demand redress for this deed of violence, but Snorri declared he could see no difference between what had happened on either side. Vigfús was ill pleased with that, and they parted in high dudgeon. In the spring Vigfús brought suit at the Thórsness Assembly for the injury of Bjorn, but Snorri countered that Bjorn had forfeited his claim to indemnity through his attack on Helgi, and the end of the matter was that Bjorn received no compensation for his wound. He carried his arm in a sling ever afterward.

CHAPTER 24

Eirík the Red discovers Greenland.

AT THIS SAME ASSEMBLY Thorgest the Old and the sons of Thórd Yeller prosecuted Eirík the Red for the slaying of Thorgest's sons, who had been slain in the fall when Eirík fetched his planking beams at Breidabólstead. That assembly was very crowded, and before that both parties had kept large bodies of armed men at their farms. About the time of the assembly, Eirík made his ship ready to put to sea in Eiríksvág on Oxnaey Island. Eirík was supported by Thorbjorn Vífilsson and Víga-Styr and the sons of Thorbrand from the Álptafirth and Eyjólf Æsuson from Swine Isle, but Styr was the only one of Eirík's backers present at the assembly. He drew as many men away from Thorgest's side as he could. Styr requested Snorri godi not to attack Eirík after the assembly with the followers of Thorgest, and promised in return that he would back Snorri at some other time in case he had any trouble of his own. And because of this promise of Styr, Snorri did not press the suit. After the assembly Thorgest and his followers went to the islands with many boats; but Eyjólf Æsuson hid Eirík's ship in Dímunarvág Bay, and Styr and Thorbjorn joined him there. Thereupon Eyjólf and Styr followed Arnkel's example: they accompanied Eirík, each in his own boat, out to sea past the island of Ellidaey.

On that voyage Eirík the Red discovered Greenland and remained there for three years. Then he returned to Iceland, where he lived for one winter before going back to colonize Greenland. That was fourteen years before Christianity was established by law in Iceland.[1]

---

[1]This agrees with the statement of the historian Ari the Learned. Christianity was adopted in Iceland in the year 1000 A.D. by the Althing as the religion of the land, after heated debate and much opposition.

CHAPTER 25

Vermund gives the two berserkers he has received from Earl Hákon to his brother Styr.

Now TO TELL ABOUT Vermund and Thórarin the Black. They made land near the mouth of the Trondheim Firth and sailed into the firth. At that time Earl Hákon Sigurdarson was ruler in Norway, and Vermund sought him out and became his retainer. Thórarin sailed westward over the North Sea that same autumn together with Álfgeir. Vermund made over to them his share of the ship. Thórarin plays no part in this saga from here on.

Earl Hákon resided at Hladir that winter. Vermund was with him and they were on good terms. The earl treated him well because he knew that Vermund came of a great family out here in Iceland.

With the earl were two brothers, Swedes by extraction, the one named Halli and the other Leiknir. They were men of such great size and strength that there was no one their equal at that time in Norway and far and wide elsewhere. They sometimes went berserk; and when they were in this state, they did not behave like human beings but went about like mad dogs and feared neither fire nor iron. Usually, however, they were not difficult to deal with if they were not antagonized. But they became extremely violent when anyone fell afoul of them. Eirík the Victorious, King of the Swedes, had sent the berserkers to the earl with the admonition that he should treat them well. He said, as was true, that they could be of the greatest assistance if due regard were taken of their disposition.

In the spring, when Vermund had been with the earl for one winter, he was eager to return to Iceland, and he asked the earl for leave to make this voyage. The earl said he might sail if he wished to, but asked him, before doing so, to consider—"if there are any things, more than others, which you would like to accept from me—such as might be to your advantage and redound to the honor and credit of both of us."

When Vermund reflected about what things he might request of the earl, it occurred to him that it would be of great advantage to him in Iceland if he had such followers as these berserkers. And the thought fixed itself in his mind that he would ask the earl if he would let him have the berserkers as a bodyguard. An additional reason for his request was that it seemed to him that his brother Styr was encroaching on his property and dealing unfairly with him as he did with most other people whenever he got the chance. He thought that Styr would reckon him less easy to deal with if he had such followers as these brothers. So Vermund told the earl that he would feel honored if he gave him the berserkers for his protection and support.

The earl replied, "Now you have asked for the one thing, it seems to me, from which you would derive no benefit even if I were to grant it to you. I am afraid they would become stubborn and arrogant once you had them in your possession. I think it is beyond the strength of most farmers' sons to keep them under control or to overawe them, even though they have been obedient to me in their service."

Vermund said he would risk taking them if the earl gave them to him. The earl told him first to ask the berserkers if they would be willing to go with him. He did so. He asked them whether they would like to go with him to Iceland and be his followers and henchmen. In return, he promised to treat them well and to grant them those things which seemed of importance to them and which they would ask of him. The berserkers declared that they had not thought of going to Iceland and that they doubted that there were chieftains there whom they would care to serve—"but if you are so anxious, Vermund, to have us go to Iceland with you, you must know for certain that we shall take it much amiss if you do not grant us any one thing we ask for if it is within your power."

Vermund assured them that this would never happen. So they agreed to go along to Iceland if that was the earl's will. Thereupon Vermund told the earl how things had gone.

The earl then made the decision that the berserkers should sail with Vermund to Iceland—"if you believe that this will redound to your honor," but he asked him to bear in mind that he would consider it an affront if they came to a bad end now that they were in his power. But Vermund declared that he need have no concern about that. Thereupon Vermund set sail for Iceland with the berserkers, and had a good passage, and came home to his farm at Bjarnarhaven the same summer in which Eirík the Red first sailed to Greenland, as was written above.

No sooner did Vermund arrive at his home farm than the berserker Halli broached the question of marriage. He asked him to make a seemly match for him. But Vermund thought there was little hope that any woman of good family would tie herself and her future in marriage to a berserker, and so he tried to evade the question. But when Halli realized this, he assumed an impudent and unmanageable attitude toward Vermund, and they were completely at odds. The berserkers were arrogant and rebellious, so that Vermund began to regret that he had ever taken them on.

In the fall Vermund prepared a great feast to which he invited Arnkel godi and the people of Eyr and also his brother Styr. And when the feast was over, Vermund offered to give Arnkel the berserkers and declared it to be a gift most suitable to him, but Arnkel declined it. Then Vermund sought advice from Arnkel as to how he could rid himself of this trouble. Arnkel urged him to give them to Styr and said he was best fitted to have such men because of his own overbearing and unscrupulous nature.

When Styr was ready to leave, Vermund went up to him and said, "Now I wish, brother, that we lay aside the hard feeling that existed between us before I went abroad and that we behave like good and friendly kinsmen. To this end I will give you the men I have brought out to Iceland with me, to assist you in strengthening your position. I doubt if any one would dare to start a fight with you if you have such followers as they are."

Styr replied, "I quite concur with you, brother, that our relationship as kinsmen should improve! But from all I have heard about those men you brought with you, any one who takes them on must expect trouble from them rather than help and advantage. I don't ever want them in my household, since my unpopularity is great enough as it is without risking additional trouble because of them."

"What advice can you give me then, kinsman," asked Vermund, "that I may rid myself of this difficulty?"

"It is one thing," said Styr, "to help you out of this trouble, and another that I should accept these men from you as a gift of friendship. This I will not do. But as to your trouble, no one is so much called on to get you out of it as I am if we can get along together."

But even though Styr stated this positively, Vermund insisted on his taking on the berserkers; and with that the two brothers parted in good friendship. Then Styr went home and the berserkers with him, even though they were not inclined to do so, declaring that Vermund had no right to sell them or give them away like thralls. Yet they said it was more to their liking to follow Styr than Vermund, and they got along quite well at first.

The berserkers accompanied Styr when he crossed the Broad Firth to kill Thorbjorn Kjálki, who lived at Kjálkafjord. He had a strong bed closet built of planks, but the berserkers immediately broke it open by forcing the joints apart.[1] And yet it was Styr who killed Thorbjorn Kjálki.

---

[1]The strongly built bed closets, which could be locked from the inside, had room for one or more beds. These sleeping places were built along the outside wall of the hall or sitting room.

CHAPTER 26

Vigfús sends a slave to kill Snorri and is himself killed by Snorri.

THE SAME FALL in which the berserkers came to Styr, it happened that Vigfús of Drápuhlíd went to burn charcoal at the place called Seljabrekkur, and with him were three of his slaves. One of them was named Svart the Strong. When they came into the forest, Vigfús said, "It's a great shame, Svart, and so it must seem to you also, that you should be a bondsman, you who are so powerful and look so manly."

"It certainly does seem a great shame to me," he replied, "but there isn't anything I can do about it."

Vigfús asked, "What will you do in return if I give you your liberty?"

Svart replied, "I can't buy my liberty with money because I have none, but there are few things I would shrink from doing to obtain my freedom."

Vigfús said, "I want you to go to Helgafell and slay Snorri godi. And when you have done that, I shall certainly give you your liberty and other good things to boot."

"That I won't be able to manage," said Svart.

"I shall propose a way," said Vigfús, "by which you can manage it without danger to your life."

"Let me hear it," replied Svart.

"You are to go to Helgafell and get up into the loft above the entrance hall near the door. Pull up some of the boards so that you can thrust a halberd through. When Snorri comes out to ease himself, thrust your halberd through the floor of the loft into Snorri's back so hard that it comes out of his belly. Then jump onto the roof, and down from the wall, and let the darkness of night take care of you."

With this design in mind Svart went to Helgafell. He pulled out some boards in the roof above the outer door and so got into the loft. He did that while Snorri and his men were sitting by the meal fires.[1] In those days they had outhouses on the farms. When Snorri and his men left the fireside to go out and ease themselves, Snorri was in the lead and had got through the door before Svart could make his lunge. Már Hallvardsson went next after Snorri, and Svart thrust at him with his halberd. The blow struck him on the shoulder blade and came out below the arm, but it did not make a serious wound. Svart jumped out and down from the wall. His feet slipped on the pavement when he landed, and he had a hard fall; and Snorri managed to grab him before he could regain his feet. Then they got the truth out of him. He told them everything that he and Vigfús had planned and also that Vigfús just then was burning charcoal below Seljabrekkur. Then Már's wound was bandaged.

---

[1] I.e., the long fires on the floor of the hall, with the benches on either side.

After that Snorri went to Drápuhlíd with six men. When they came up the hillside, they saw the fire where Vigfús and his people were burning charcoal. They came upon them unawares and killed Vigfús, but gave his men servants quarter. Then Snorri went home, and Vigfús' men servants brought the news to Drápuhlíd. Vigfús was placed in a mound the following day; and that same day Thorgerd, the wife of Vigfús, went in to Bólstead to inform her kinsman Arnkel. She asked him to assume the prosecution for the slaying of Vigfús,[2] but he refused. He declared that this was the responsibility of Vigfús' relatives, the Kjalleklings, and pointed out that this case could best be handled by Styr. He said that it was Styr's duty to take up the prosecution, and all the more so since he was eager to meddle in so many other affairs.

Thormód Trefilsson spoke this verse regarding the slaying of Vigfús:

20. Felled the folkruler
     first the golden-bristled-
     helmet's owner,[3] him
     who hight was Vigfús;
     rent sithen ravenous
     ravens there the lifeless
     body, blood-bespattered,
     of Bjorn's inheritor.

---

[2] It was difficult for women and minors to handle the prosecution of such cases. See what is said in Chap. 38.

[3] Kenning for 'warrior'. Helmets often were surmounted by the figure of a boar. This stanza as well as the others by Thormód Trefilsson (26, 33, 34, 35) are in the measure called *Haðarlag,* different from the Eddic *Málaháttr* by having internal rimes (not attempted here).

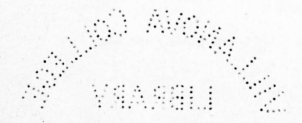

CHAPTER 27

Vigfús' widow obtains Arnkel's promise to prosecute Snorri.

THEREUPON THORGERD went to Styr's place below Hraun and asked Styr to take up the prosecution for the slaying of his kinsman Vigfús.

He replied, "This I promised Snorri godi last spring, when he remained neutral during my litigation with the clan of Thorgest, that I would not oppose him in any case if there were many other kinsmen of mine as much involved as I. Why don't you appeal to my brother Vermund in this matter or to other relatives of ours?"

Thereupon she went to Bjarnarhaven and asked Vermund for his support, declaring that it concerned him most—"seeing that Vigfús had the most confidence in you of all his kinsmen."

Vermund replied, "I am indeed obligated to do something for you, but I am not inclined to do anything in this difficult affair ahead of the rest of our kinsmen. I shall lend my assistance, in word and deed, such as I am able to. But first I want you to go out to Eyr and talk to Vigfús' kinsman Steinthór. He doesn't mind a fight, and it is about time for him to prove himself in some litigation or other."

Thorgerd said, "Much labor you impose upon me in this business, but I shall spare no effort if it will help to further it."

Then she went out to Eyr and talked to Steinthór and asked him to take the lead in the prosecution.

Steinthór replied, "Why do you ask this of me? I am a young man and have had no experience in litigation. And those kinsmen of Vigfús who are more closely related to him than I are also more aggressive than I am. You can hardly expect that I should take this case off their hands. However, I shall not fail to assist those of my kinsmen who have the responsibility for this lawsuit."

Thorgerd received no other answer from him. So then she re-crossed the fjords back to Vermund and told him how things had gone. She declared that the entire case would collapse unless he assumed the leadership.

Vermund said, "Rather, there is great hope still that there will be an energetic prosecution of this case that will give you satisfaction. I shall propose one more plan to you if you care to follow it."

She replied, "I will do almost anything to accomplish my purpose."

"Then go home," said Vermund, "and have the body of your husband Vigfús dug up. Then take his head and bring it to Arnkel and tell him that this head would not have left to others the prosecution for *his* slaying if that had been imperative."[1]

Thorgerd said she did not know how successful such a plan would be, but she said she did see that they were sparing her neither humiliation nor labor—"but I will do it," she said, "if it will serve to bring down the overbearing of my enemies."

After that she went home and carried out this plan just as she had been instructed. When she came to Bólstead, she told Arnkel that all of Vigfús' kinsmen wanted him to be the leader of the prosecution for the slaying of Vigfús and that they all promised him their assistance. Arnkel declared that he had already stated his position in this matter.

Then Thorgerd quickly drew the head from underneath her cloak and said, "Here is the head that would not have excused itself from taking up the prosecution for you if that had been necessary."

Arnkel shuddered at this and pushed her away and said, "Go back and tell the kinsmen of Vigfús not to hold back more in supporting me against Snorri godi than I do in the management of the prosecution. But something tells me that no matter how this matter turns out, they will be seeking the lee shore before I do. And I see now that it is the advice of Vermund you are following. I do not need to be egged on by him, whatever the circumstances in which we kinsmen are placed."

Thereupon Thorgerd went home. The winter passed. In the spring Arnkel initiated the prosecution for the suit concerning the slaying of Vigfús against all those men who had been involved in the slaying except Snorri godi. Snorri on his part brought a countersuit to have Vigfús declared fallen as an outlaw for having plotted against his life and for the wounding of Már. Both sides went to the Thórsness Assembly with many followers. All the Kjalleklings backed Arnkel, and they were the more numerous. Arnkel upheld his suit with great energy. And when the cases came before the court, men intervened to have them submitted for arbitration with the good services and proposals for terms

---

[1] Similar expedients for rousing friend or kinsman to exact vengeance occur frequently in the sagas.

by men of good will. The outcome was that Snorri godi by handclasp
agreed to abide by the arbitration, and then large fines were assessed.
Már was to be banished from Iceland for three years.[2] Snorri paid the
fines. The assembly concluded with all suits settled by mutual
agreement.

---

[2]It may seem curious to our sense of justice that it was Már who should be
banished; but any kinsman of the chief defendant "would do." And in this case
it might have suited Snorri's convenience better to have his manager go into
exile than himself.

CHAPTER 28

*The berserker Halli desires Styr's daughter in marriage. Styr slays both
berserkers.*

NOW TO TELL of what happened next: as was put down before, the
berserkers were now staying with Styr; and when they had been there
for a while, Halli entered into conversation with Ásdís, Styr's daughter.
She was a young and accomplished woman, vain and showy and rather
haughty. When Styr learned that they had been talking together, he
asked Halli not to cause him disgrace or vexation by beguiling his
daughter.

Halli replied, "It is no disgrace to you if I talk to your daughter, and
I am not doing so to bring shame upon you. Let me tell you at once
that I have taken such a strong liking to her that I cannot put her out
of my mind. Now I wish," continued Halli, "to be fast friends with
you and to ask you to give me your daughter Ásdís in marriage. In return, I shall offer you my friendship and faithful following and such
powerful backing, with the support of my brother Leiknir, that in Iceland there shall not be found such great renown through the service
of two men as we two shall afford you. Our prowess will strengthen
your chieftainship more than if you were to marry your daughter to the

most prominent farmer in the Broad Firth District. This will compensate for the fact that we two are not wealthy. But if you will not grant me this request, that will put an end to our friendship; and then each of us will proceed as suits him best. And then it will not do you any good to complain about my talking with Ásdís."

When he had said this, Styr fell silent and was at a loss for a reply; but after a while he said, "I wonder if you were speaking in full earnest, or was that merely idle chatter and an attempt to start a quarrel?"

"I shall want you to answer," said Halli, "knowing that this is not merely empty talk. Our friendship depends entirely on how you answer this proposal."

"In that case," Styr replied, "I shall want to discuss this matter with my friends and take counsel with them what answer to make."

Halli said, "Discuss the matter with anyone you wish, but within the next three days. I do not want to have your reply postponed longer than that, because I do not care to be a poor wooer." With that they parted.

On the following morning Styr rode to Helgafell. When he arrived there, Snorri offered him his hospitality; but Styr said he wanted to discuss something with him and then ride home again. Snorri asked whether he had some troublesome problem to talk over.

"So it seems to me," said Styr.

Snorri replied, "In that case let us go up to the top of Helgafell, for the plans which have been devised there have rarely been thwarted."

Thereupon they went up to the top of the hill. They sat there conversing until evening, but no one knew what they talked about. Afterward Styr rode home.

The next morning he and Halli discussed matters. Halli asked Styr to what conclusion he had come about his proposal.

Styr said, "People say that you are a man without possessions; so what do you propose to do to make up for that, seeing that you have no goods to offer?"

Halli replied, "I will do what I can, but I can't offer money when I have none."

"I understand," said Styr, "that you will take it amiss if I do not give you my daughter to wife. So I am going to do as men did in the olden days. I shall let you earn this marriage by accomplishing some great deeds."

"What might these be?" asked Halli.

"You are to clear a pathway," said Styr, "over the lava field over to

Bjarnarhaven and build a boundary wall across the lava between my
lands and those of Vermund. Then you are to construct a sheep enclosure on my land on the lava field. When you have done all that,
I shall give you my daughter Ásdís in marriage."

Halli replied, "I am not accustomed to that sort of work, and yet
I will agree to this if it will serve to attain this woman in marriage."

Styr said they could come to an agreement on these terms.

Thereupon the berserkers began to clear the pathway, and it was
an immense labor they performed. They also built the wall, traces
of which can still be seen. And after that they built the enclosure. While
they were occupied with this work, Styr had a bath dug down into the
ground at his place. There was a window above the oven so that
water could be poured in from the outside. That room was extremely
hot. On the last day, when the two tasks were almost completed and
they were working on the sheep pen, Ásdís, Styr's daughter, walked
past them. That was near the farmstead. She had put on her finest
clothing. But when Halli and his companion accosted her, she did not
answer. Then Halli spoke this verse:

21. Whither, Gerd-of-gold-rings,[1]
    gait-fair maiden—neither
    lie about that, lady
    linen-dight—now goest thou?
    because all winter, winsome
    woman, never saw I,
    queenly keeper-of-the-
    coffers,[1] thee so well-clad.

Then Leiknir spoke this verse:

22. Higher head-gear[2] rarely
    has the fir-of-gold-rings[3]
    ever worn, nor, either,
    armlets borne more precious.
    What, thou Hlín-of-flax, is
    hidden, more than to us is

---

[1]Kenning for 'woman'.

[2]The high, starched head-dress is worn by Icelandic women in their holiday
costume even now.

[3]The names of trees often serve as the basic word for kennings for men or
women.

seen, of spite, fair-spoken
spouse, under this finery?

After that they parted. The berserkers went home that evening and
were very tired, as is the nature of men who go berserk, that all their
strength leaves them once their rage ebbs. Styr went out to meet them
and thanked them for their work and invited them to use the bath and
rest afterward. They did so. And when they had entered the bath
room, Styr had it closed and rocks piled on the trapdoor above the
entrance. He had a raw oxhide spread before the entrance. Then he
had water poured in through the opening above the oven. Then the
bath became so hot that the berserkers could not endure it, and they
ran for the door. Halli was able to break open the trapdoor and jump
out, but he slipped on the oxhide and Styr gave him his death blow.
Then when Leiknir tried to get up through the door, Styr thrust his
spear through him, and he fell back into the bath and died there. Thereupon Styr had the bodies cared for, and they were taken out to a hollow
in the lava and rocks were heaped on them. This hollow is so deep that
one can see nothing from it except the sky above. It is close by the
pathway. Over the burial place of the berserkers, Styr spoke this verse:

23. Dangerous and difficult my
     daughter's suitor ever,
     the swaggering sword-wielder,
     seemed to me to deal with.
     In dread I dwell no more of
     dour warrior's overbearing:
     promptly the pair by me
     places of rest were given.

When Snorri godi heard of this, he rode to Styr's place below Hraun,
and he and Styr again fell to talking together all day long. The outcome of their talk was that Styr betrothed his daughter Ásdís to Snorri
godi, and the marriage took place the following autumn. People said
that both became more powerful through this alliance. Snorri was
shrewder and more of a planner, while Styr was more aggressive. Both
had many kinsmen and followers in the district.

CHAPTER 29

*Thórodd obtains part of Earl Sigurd's treasure. —Bjorn's love affair
with Thórodd's wife Thurid.*

THERE WAS A MAN named Thórodd who was descended from the
people of Medalfell Strands. He was an honest sort of man. He was a
great merchant and was the owner of trading ships. Thórodd had made
a merchant voyage from Norway west to Ireland, to Dublin. At that
time Sigurd Hlodvesson, Earl of the Orkneys, had been harrying in
the Hebrides and as far west as the Isle of Man.[1] He exacted tribute
from the inhabitants of Man. When they had come to terms with him,
the earl left men there to wait for the tribute, most of which was paid
in pure silver. The earl himself, however, proceeded north to the Orkneys. And when the men who had collected the tax were ready to set
sail, they got a wind from the southwest. But when they had sailed a
while, the wind shifted to the southeast and then to the east and developed into a mighty storm. They were driven north of Ireland, and
their ship was dashed to pieces on an uninhabited island. And when
they had gotten into this situation, Thórodd the Icelander, who was on
his way from Dublin, came close to them. The earl's men called to the
merchantmen for help. Thórodd had the boat lowered and got into it
himself. And when they met, the earl's men implored Thórodd to help
them and offered to pay him if he would take them to the Orkneys to
Earl Sigurd. But Thórodd did not think he could do that since he was
bound for Iceland. They entreated him to do so because they believed
both their possessions and their liberty were at stake if they were set
ashore in Ireland or the Hebrides, where they had harried before. So,
finally, he sold them the boat from his seagoing ship, for which he received a large share of the tribute money. Thereupon they set their
course for the Orkneys in the boat, and Thórodd sailed to Iceland
without a boat. He made land in the south, then set a westward course
and sailed into the Broad Firth, and arrived safely at Dogurdarness. In
the fall he went to stay with Snorri godi at Helgafell. After that he was

---

[1]Which is, of course, south of the Hebrides.

called Thórodd Skattkaupandi.[2] All this occurred after the slaying of Thorbjorn the Stout. Snorri's sister Thuríd, who had been married to Thorbjorn the Stout, was living at Helgafell that winter. And soon after he had returned to Iceland, Thórodd asked Snorri godi to give him his sister Thuríd in marriage. And since he was wealthy, and since Snorri knew all about him and realized that she very much required guardianship—for all these reasons Snorri considered it wise to marry her to him; and he arranged for their marriage during the winter there at Helgafell. In the following spring Thórodd settled at Fródá and became a good and dependable farmer.

As soon as Thuríd came to Fródá, Bjorn Ásbrandsson began to pay visits there regularly; and the general opinion was that there was some dalliance between him and Thuríd. Thórodd objected to these visits but did not pursue the matter. At that time Thórir Woodenleg was living at Arnarhvál. His sons, Orn and Valr, were then fully grown and were young men of great promise. They reproached Thórodd for enduring such disgrace as Bjorn was bringing upon him and offered him their support if he wished to put a stop to Bjorn's visits.

One time Bjorn came to Fródá and sat talking with Thuríd. Thórodd was always in the habit of staying inside when Bjorn was there, but now he was nowhere to be seen.

Thuríd said, "Be careful on your way home, Bjorn, for I believe that Thórodd now intends to bring to an end your coming here. I think they have gone ahead to set an ambush for you, and he will have it so arranged that you won't meet on even terms."

Then Bjorn spoke this verse:

24. Together would we gladly,
     golden woods and heaven
     between—but trials await us—
     tarrying spend long hours,
     but that, this very night, I
     think I shall in sorrow,
     goddess-of-gold,[3] drink to
     gladness now gone forever.

Thereupon Bjorn took his weapons and left, intending to go home. But when he came up past Digramúli, five men jumped up in front of

---

[2] 'Tribute-bargainer'.
[3] Kenning for 'woman'.

him. They were Thórodd, two of his men servants, and the sons of
Thórir Woodenleg. They attacked Bjorn, but he defended himself skilfully and bravely. The sons of Thórir pressed him the hardest. They
inflicted wounds upon him, but he succeeded in killing them both. After
that Thórodd and his two servants fled. He was lightly wounded, and
they not at all. Bjorn continued on his way until he came home. He
went into the sitting room. The mistress of the house asked a serving
woman to assist him;[4] and when she came into the room with a light,
she saw that Bjorn was all bloody. She then went and told Ásbrand, his
father, that Bjorn had come home completely covered with blood.
Ásbrand went into the room and asked Bjorn why he was so bloody—
"or did you and Thórodd have a clash?" Bjorn answered and said
that that was the case. Ásbrand asked how the fight had turned out.
Bjorn spoke this verse:

25. Harder for hard-fighting
hero 't will be to fight me—
indeed 't was I who did to
death both sons of Vidlegg—
than to kiss the comely
keeper-of-head-dresses,[5]
or for the bow-bender
brave to gain his treasure.[6]

Thereupon Ásbrand bandaged his wounds, and he recovered completely.

Thórodd sought Snorri's aid in the prosecution for the killing of the
sons of Thórir, and Snorri had the case prepared for the Thórsness Assembly. The sons of Thorlák at Eyr gave the Breidavík people their
backing. The case ended in this fashion that Ásbrand by handclasp assumed responsibility for his son Bjorn and paid the fines for the killings.
Bjorn was sentenced to three years of exile, and he went abroad that
same summer. That summer, too, Thuríd of Fródá gave birth to a boy
child, and he was named Kjartan. He grew up at home at Fródá and
soon became a large and promising lad.

---

[4]Viz., to help him pull off his outer garments.
[5]Kenning for 'woman'.
[6]Ironic reference to the not very warlike Thórodd and his rather ignominious
acquisition of the tribute.

As soon as Bjorn came to Norway,[7] he continued south to Denmark
and from there to Jómsborg. At that time Palnatóki was the leader of
the Jómsvikings. Bjorn joined them by submitting to their rules and
gained the reputation of a brave warrior. He was at Jómsborg when
Styrbjorn the Strong conquered it. Bjorn also went to Sweden when
the Jómsvikings aided Styrbjorn, and he was in the battle on the
Fyrisvellir in which Styrbjorn was killed. He escaped into the forest
with other Jómsvikings. As long as Palnatóki was alive, Bjorn remained
with him and was regarded as a man of honor and one of the bravest in
all dangers.

---

[7]After reaching the nearest point in Norway, shipping followed the coastal route
to the Baltic.

CHAPTER 30

Thórólf Lamefoot robs Úlfar's hay.

Now to tell about Thórólf Lamefoot. He began to age greatly, and
with that he became mean and violent and entirely indifferent to other
people's rights. Also, he and his son got along worse as time passed.

One day Thórólf rode to Úlfarsfell to see farmer Úlfar. Úlfar was
skilful at farm work and was noted for gathering in his hay more
quickly than other men. He was also so lucky with his livestock that
none ever died of starvation or of killing diseases. When they met,
Thórólf asked Úlfar what advice he could give him about managing his
farm work, and how he thought the summer would be, and whether
there would be good drying weather.

Úlfar replied, "I can't give you any better advice than what I follow
myself. I am going to have the scythes brought out today and have as
much hay mowed as possible all this week, for I am thinking that it will

turn rainy. But I believe that after that there will be good drying weather for the next half month."

All happened just as he foretold, for it often turned out that he was better at predicting the weather than others. After seeing Úlfar, Thórólf went back to his farm. He had many farm workers at his place, and he had them start haying at once. The weather turned out to be as Úlfar had predicted. Thórólf and Úlfar owned a meadow in common up on the ridge. Both first cut much hay, then dried it, and piled it in large hayricks. One morning Thórólf got up early and looked out. The weather was thick and he thought the dry spell was going to come to an end, so he ordered his slaves to get up and pile up the hay and to work as hard as they could all day—"for I don't think the weather can be trusted." The slaves got dressed and went out to make hay. Thórólf loaded the hay on the pack animals,[1] while urging his slaves on to get as much done as they could.

That same morning Úlfar went out early to look around, and when he came in, his workmen asked him about the weather. He told them to sleep in peace. "The weather is fine," he said. "It will clear up. You are to cut hay in the homefield today, but tomorrow we shall bring in the hay which we have up on the ridge."

The weather turned out just as he had said. Toward evening Úlfar sent a man up on the ridge to see about the hay which was stacked there. Thórólf had had the hay brought in on three pack animals at a time during the day, and by early afternoon they had brought in all that belonged to him. Then he ordered them to bring Úlfar's hay into his own enclosure. They did as they were told. But when the man sent by Úlfar saw that, he ran and told Úlfar. Úlfar hurried up on the ridge. He was quite furious and asked why Thórólf was stealing from him. Thórólf declared he didn't care what he said. He used violent language and was difficult to deal with, so that the two were on the verge of coming to blows. Úlfar realized that there was nothing for him to do but to leave. He went to Arnkel and told him about the loss he had sustained and asked him for support; or else, he said, things would go badly for him. Arnkel promised to ask his father to pay for the hay, but he added he had a dark foreboding that it would do no good. And when father and son met, Arnkel asked his father to make up to Úlfar for the theft of the hay; but Thórólf said that that slave was far too wealthy anyway. Arnkel asked him to do it for his sake. Thórólf de-

---

[1] No wheeled vehicles were used in Iceland in the olden days.

clared he would do nothing for that reason except to worsen the lot of Úlfar, and with that they parted.

When Arnkel saw Úlfar again, he told him what answer Thórólf had given him. Úlfar showed clearly that he thought that Arnkel had not taken a strong stand and said he could very well get his father to listen to him if he really had a mind to. Arnkel paid Úlfar what he wanted for the hay; and when the two kinsmen met again, Arnkel requested the price of the hay from his father once more. Thórólf's answer wasn't a whit more conciliatory, however, and the two parted in anger. During the following autumn Arnkel had seven oxen which belonged to his father driven down from the mountain pasture and slaughtered at his farm. Thórólf was greatly provoked at this and demanded the value of the oxen from Arnkel, but Arnkel said that they should be regarded as compensation for Úlfar's hay. Then Thórólf grew even more enraged than before. He declared that all this was of Úlfar's doing and said that he would have to pay for it.

CHAPTER 31

Thórólf sets fire to Úlfar's house and seeks Snorri's aid.

THE FOLLOWING WINTER during the Yule season Thórólf gave a great banquet and treated his slaves liberally with drink. And when they were drunk, he egged them on to go to Úlfarsfell and burn Úlfar to death in his house, in return for which he promised to give them their liberty. The slaves said they would do that to obtain their liberty if he kept his promise. Then six of them went to Úlfarsfell. They took a pile of wood, dragged it to the building, and set it on fire. At the same time Arnkel was having a feast at Bólstead; and when he and his guests were going to bed, they saw the fire at Úlfarsfell. They hastened over, caught the slaves, and put out the fire. The buildings had not been damaged very much. On the following morning Arnkel had all the slaves taken to the Vadilshofdi Promontory and hanged there. Then Úlfar made over all of his property to Arnkel and thereby placed himself under Arnkel's protection. This agreement angered the sons of Thorbrand, for they had believed they would inherit all of Úlfar's property after his death since he was their freedman. And for this reason a considerable coolness developed between Arnkel and the sons of Thorbrand, so that they could no longer engage in games together. Before that time they had played ball together,[1] and Arnkel was the strongest at the game; the one who could best compete with him and was the second strongest was a man named Freystein Bófi. He was a foster child and the alleged son of Thorbrand. At least, most people thought that he was his son and that a bondwoman was his mother. Freystein was an excellent sort of man and one of importance. Thórólf Lamefoot was furious with Arnkel when his slaves were killed, and demanded compensation, but Arnkel flatly refused to pay a penny for them. This made Thórólf more furious than ever.

One day Thórólf rode to Helgafell to have a talk with Snorri godi. Snorri invited him to stay there, but Thórólf said he did not need to eat his food. "I have come here to have you help me obtain justice, since I regard you as my district chieftain and therefore obligated to obtain justice for men who have been unfairly dealt with."

"Who is wronging you, farmer Thórólf?" asked Snorri.

"My son Arnkel," replied Thorolf.

Snorri said, "You should not make that accusation. Indeed, you should think in all matters as Arnkel does, for he is a better man than you."

"That isn't so," he retorted, "for he is riding roughshod over me. I want to have your good friendship now, Snorri, and I want you to take up the matter of indemnity for my slaves, and in that case I won't claim all the compensation for myself."

Snorri answered, "I do not wish to become involved in a quarrel between you and your son."

Thórólf replied, "You are no friend of Arnkel's. Perhaps you think I am tightfisted, but this won't be the case now. I know you would like to get hold of Krákuness and the forest on it, which is the greatest prize here in the district. Now I shall make over all of that to you if you will

---

[1] Ball games were very popular among the Icelanders and were played most strenuously.

take up the prosecution for the killing of my slaves and carry it out so vigorously that you will increase your influence, and they who have done me that shame will realize they have gone too far. Nor do I want any man who was involved here to be spared, even though he be more or less a relative of mine."

Snorri felt a great urge to own the forest, and it is said that he accepted the offer of the land and assumed the prosecution for the killing of the slaves. Thórólf then rode home quite pleased with himself, but this deal did not win much approval from people.

In the fall Snorri preferred charges against Arnkel at the Thórsness Assembly for having slain Thórólf's slaves. Both were accompanied to the assembly by many followers. Snorri prosecuted the case; and when it came before the court, Arnkel demanded a verdict of acquittal on the testimony of five neighbors and cited as a point for the defense the fact that the slaves had been caught in the act of setting fire to the buildings. Snorri raised this objection, that the slaves could have been killed with impunity at the place where they committed the crime—"but when you led them up on the Vadilshofdi Promontory and killed them there, then I hold that there they were not outside the law." Snorri carried his point and rendered void Arnkel's demand for acquittal. After that, men intervened to bring about a settlement, and an agreement was arrived at. The two brothers, Styr and Vermund, were to arbitrate the case. They awarded as compensation twelve ounces of silver for each of the slaves. The money was to be paid at the assembly. And when the fine was paid, Snorri gave the purse to Thórólf. He took it and said, "I did not think, when I gave you my land, that you would follow up the case with so little energy. But this I know: Arnkel would not have denied me such paltry indemnity as I got here for my slaves if I had left the settlement to him."

Snorri replied, "I will say this, that you did not come off badly at all, but I shall never again hazard my honor for your malice and wickedness."

Thórólf retorted, "Neither is there much likelihood that I shall ever again seek your support in any litigation, and I am thinking this will not be the last trouble to befall the people of this district."

After that people left the assembly. Both Arnkel and Snorri were much irked by this outcome of the case, but Thórólf most of all.

CHAPTER 32

Spá-Gils kills Úlfar. —Arnkel maintains his possession of Úlfar's estate against the sons of Thorbrand.

WE ARE NOW TOLD that Orlyg at Orlygsstead took sick; and when this illness grew worse, Úlfar, his brother, cared for him. He died of this illness. As soon as Orlyg was dead, Úlfar sent for Arnkel; and he immediately came, and he and Úlfar took possession of all the property there. When the sons of Thorbrand learned of the passing of Orlyg, they went to Orlygsstead and laid claim to the property there and declared that everything owned by this man to whom they had given his liberty belonged to them. Úlfar, however, insisted that he was the legal heir of his brother. They asked Arnkel which side he intended to support. Arnkel declared that, if he had his way, Úlfar should not be robbed by anyone as long as their fellowship lasted. The sons of Thorbrand then left the place and first of all went to Helgafell to tell Snorri godi what had happened and to request his backing. But Snorri said he would not fight with Arnkel about this, seeing that they had dillydallied so long that Arnkel and Úlfar had been able to get their hands on the property first. The sons of Thorbrand declared that Snorri was not likely to prevail in more important affairs if he did not take a hand in this.

In the fall of that year Arnkel held a great autumn feast. It was his custom to invite his friend Úlfar to all banquets and present him with gifts at parting. On the day people were about to leave the party at Bólstead, Thórólf left his place to visit his friend Spá-Gils[1]—he lived in Thórsárdale at Spágilsstead—and asked him to ride along with him to Úlfarsfell Ridge. One of Thórólf's slaves went with him. And when they came onto the ridge, Thórólf said, "That is no doubt Úlfar down there, returning from the banquet, and more likely than not he has some costly gifts with him. Now I wish Spá-Gils," he said, "that you ride to meet him and lie in ambush under the wall at Úlfarsfell. I want you to kill him, and for that I will give you three marks of silver. I shall take care of the fines for the manslaughter. And when you have killed

---

[1] N.B., not the same Spá-Gils who occurs in Chap. 18.

Úlfar, you are to take from him the valuables which he received from Arnkel. Then run along Úlfarsfell to Krákuness. But if any men come after you, take cover in the woods. After that come to me, and I shall see to it that no harm will befall you."

And because Spá-Gils had a great many dependents and was quite poor, he swallowed the bait and went out and sat under cover of the wall of the homefield at Úlfarsfell. Then he saw Úlfar coming up from Bólstead with the good shield and the inlaid sword which Arnkel had given him. When they met, Spá-Gils asked to see the sword. He flattered Úlfar greatly and said he was most certainly an important man, seeing that he was considered worthy of receiving such valuable gifts. Úlfar twisted his beard with pleasure and handed him both sword and shield. Gils drew the sword at once and thrust it through Úlfar. Then he ran along Úlfarsfell to Krákuness.

Arnkel was standing outside at his farm when he saw a man running with a shield, and he thought he recognized it. He was sure that Úlfar would not have surrendered the shield of his own free will. Arnkel ordered men to give pursuit—"and in case this is due to some plot my father has hatched out and this man has caused the death of Úlfar, you are to kill him on the spot, whoever he may be, and do not let him come before my eyes." Then Arnkel went up to Úlfarsfell; there they found Úlfar dead.

Thórólf Lamefoot saw Spá-Gils running along Úlfarsfell with a shield, and he guessed he knew how things had gone. He said to the slave who was accompanying him, "I want you to go to Kársstead and tell the sons of Thorbrand to hasten to Úlfarsstead so as not to be robbed of a freedman's inheritance as they were before, for now Úlfar is slain." Thereupon Thórólf rode home and thought he had scored a success.

Now the men who pursued Spá-Gils overtook him by a cliff that rises there. They then got the truth from him. And when he had confessed all and how it had come about, they put him to death and buried him there by the cliff; but the sword and shield they took and brought them to Arnkel.

Now Thórólf's slave arrived at Kársstead and delivered his message; whereupon they went to Úlfarsfell, but when they arrived there, Arnkel was already there with many men. Then the sons of Thorbrand laid claim to all the property which Úlfar had owned, but Arnkel produced the testimony of witnesses who had been present at the agreement between him and Úlfar; and he declared he would hold to that bargain, for he said that he had strictly adhered to the law in this business.[2] He asked them not to lay claim to this property because, he said, he would hold on to it as though it were his own patrimony. Then the sons of Thorbrand saw that there was nothing to do but to leave the place. Again they went to Helgafell and told Snorri godi what the situation was and asked him for his backing. Snorri said that things had gone just as before, that they had been too slow for Arnkel—"And you will not snatch this property out of the hands of Arnkel because he has already taken possession of the movable goods. But the lands lie equally close to both of you and will fall to him who is the stronger. It is all too likely that Arnkel will get the better of you as he has done in all your dealings with him. The fact is, you will share the lot of many a one, for Arnkel lords it over everyone in the district; and that will be the case so long as he lives, whether that be for a longer or shorter time."

Thorleif Kimbi answered, "You are right about that, Snorri! No wonder you will not help us to our right against Arnkel, for you are no match for him in any matter which you have to fight out with him."

After that the sons of Thorbrand went home, and they were extremely put out [about this business].

---

[2]According to Old Icelandic law the property of a childless freedman reverted to his former owner. Insofar, then, Arnkel is taking the law into his own hands. Still, Úlfar had made it over to him.

CHAPTER 33

Thórólf's death and burial.

SNORRI GODI NOW HAD Krákuness Forest worked and had much wood cut. It seemed to Thórólf Lamefoot that the forest was being ruined, so he rode to Helgafell and asked Snorri to return the forest to him. He said he had merely lent but had not given it to him. Snorri said this matter would be cleared up when the witnesses to the transaction testified. He said he would not give up the forest unless they testified against him. Thórólf left in a very ugly mood. He rode to Bólstead to see Arnkel. Arnkel received his father cordially and asked what his errand was.

Thórólf answered, "This is my reason for coming here: I see that things are not as they should be, what with this hostility between us. I wish now that we put an end to it and live on good terms as kinsmen should, for it is unseemly that we should be at odds. It seems to me that we could become powerful here in the district with your hardihood and my planning."

"I would like nothing better," said Arnkel, "than that our relations should improve."

"What I want," said Thórólf, "is that we begin our agreement and friendship by taking back Krákuness Forest from Snorri godi, for what irks me most is that he should withhold our property from us. But now he will not release the forest to me and insists that I gave it to him, but that is a lie."

Arnkel replied, "It was not out of friendship for me that you handed the forest over to Snorri, and I am not going to fight with him about the forest just on account of your malice. I know well enough that he is not legally entitled to the forest, but I don't care to reward you for your malice by the spectacle of Snorri and me litigating about it."

"I am thinking," said Thórólf, "that cowardice is the reason for your refusal rather than your not wanting me to enjoy the fight between you two."

"Have it your own way," said Arnkel, "but I am not going to begin litigation with Snorri about the forest as things stand."

With that father and son parted. Thórólf Lamefoot went home and felt exceedingly dejected about the turn matters had taken and about being thwarted in everything. He arrived home in the evening and spoke with no one. He sat down in the high seat and did not eat anything all evening. He remained sitting there after all the others had gone to bed. And in the morning when they got up, Thórólf was still sitting there and was dead. Then the mistress of the house sent a man to Arnkel to inform him of the passing of Thórólf. Arnkel rode up to Hvamm with several of his men servants. And when they came there, Arnkel learned for certain that his father was dead, sitting in the seat of honor; but all the people in the house were terrified because they all thought there was something uncanny about his death.

Arnkel now went into the kitchen and from there along the dais behind Thórólf. He warned all not to approach him from the front until
the last service to the dead had been performed.[1] Arnkel took Thórólf
by the shoulders, and he had to exert all his strength to get him down
from the high seat. Then he wrapped a cloth around Thórólf's head and
prepared the body according to the custom of that time. After that he
had the wall broken through behind him and had him pulled out through
this opening.[2] Then oxen were harnessed to a sled, Thórólf was laid in
it, and they brought him up into Thórsárdale. And it was not without
a struggle before they reached the place where he was to be buried.
They buried Thórólf securely and heaped stones over him. After that
Arnkel rode home to Hvamm and took possession of all the property
there which his father had owned. Arnkel stayed there for three days,
and nothing of particular moment happened during this time. Then he
went home.

---

[1] These rites consisted in the closing of the dead person's eyes, nostrils, and
mouth.

[2] These precautions were taken for two reasons. Wrapping a cloth around
Thórólf's head was intended to prevent him from putting the "evil eye" on anyone. Removing the body through a hole in the wall, which was then closed up
again, was to prevent the ghost of the dead man from entering the house. It
was believed that a ghost re-entered a house at the same place where the body
had been taken out.

CHAPTER 34

Thórólf haunts the neighborhood. His ghost is laid by Arnkel.

AFTER THE DEATH of Thórólf Lamefoot, it seemed to many that there
was something uncanny out of doors as soon as the sun got low. Add
to this that as the summer wore on, people became aware that Thórólf
was not lying quietly. They could never be out of doors in peace after

the sun set. And besides that the oxen which had drawn Thórólf be-
came troll-ridden, and all the cattle which came near the grave of
Thórólf went mad and bellowed until they died. The shepherd at
Hvamm was often chased home by Thórólf.

It happened one evening during the autumn at Hvamm that neither
the shepherd nor the sheep came home. In the morning a search was
made, and the shepherd was found dead a short distance from the grave
of Thórólf. He was black and blue all over, and every bone in him was
broken. He was buried near Thórólf.[1] But of all the sheep which had
been in the valley, some were found dead, and the rest ran up into the
mountains and were never found again. And if birds settled on the
grave of Thórólf, they fell down dead.

Matters became so bad that no man dared graze his livestock up in
the valley. Often during the night people at Hvamm heard loud noises
outside. They also often heard how the house was being ridden.[2] And
when winter came, Thórólf often appeared inside the house at the farm;
and he molested the mistress of the house most of all. Many a person
took harm from this, and she herself almost went mad; and it ended
with the mistress of the house dying from these apparitions. She was
also taken up to Thórsárdale and buried near Thórólf. After that
people fled from the farm. Thórólf now began to haunt the valley to
such an extent that all the farms there were deserted. And his hauntings increased so greatly in violence that he killed some men and put
others to flight. And all who had died were seen with him when he
haunted places. People made a great outcry about this trouble. It
seemed to them that it was up to Arnkel to deal with it. Arnkel invited
all those to stay with him who liked it better there than elsewhere. For
wherever Arnkel was present, there never was any injury from Thórólf
and his company. So fearful were people of the hauntings of Thórólf
that no one dared travel about during the winter even on business.
But when winter passed there came a fine spring. And when the frost
was out of the ground, Arnkel sent a man to Kársstead to the sons of
Thorbrand and asked them to go along with him to take Thórólf away
out of Thórsárdale and to find him a burial place elsewhere. All men
were then equally obligated by law to participate in the burial of the

---

[1] Like Thórólf's wife, he is buried there to propitiate Thórólf or to keep him
company.

[2] It is frequently mentioned in the sagas that revenants bestrode the house gables
and that the nightmare rode the livestock to death.

dead (as they are now) if they were summoned. But when the sons of Thorbrand heard that, they said it was no concern of theirs to help Arnkel or any of his followers out of their difficulties.

Then old Thorbrand spoke. "It is necessary," he said, "to go on all those errands to which people are obligated by law, and you have now been requested to do something which you ought not to refuse."

Then Thórodd said to the messenger, "Go and tell Arnkel that I shall come for my brothers. I shall be at Úlfarsfell and meet him there."

Now the messenger went and told Arnkel this. He made ready, and there were twelve men in all. They had with them a sledge and oxen and tools for digging. They first went to Úlfarsfell and met Thórodd there. He had two other men with him. They crossed the ridge over to Thórsárdale to the mound of Thórólf. They opened it and found the body of Thórólf there undecomposed and most hideous to look at. They lifted him out of the grave and laid him on the sledge and harnessed two strong oxen to it. They dragged him up to Úlfarsfell Ridge, and by then the oxen were spent. Others were hitched up, and they dragged him up on the ridge. Arnkel intended to move him to the Vadilshofdi Promontory and bury him there. But when they came in to the edge of the hill, the oxen went mad. They broke away, ran down off the ridge, and headed out along the mountain side above the fence at Úlfarsfell and out toward the sea, and by that time they were completely spent. And Thórólf was so heavy by then that they were scarcely able to move him at all. So they took him to a little headland nearby and buried him there, and that place has since been called Bægifótshofdi ('Lame-foot's Headland'). Later Arnkel had a wall built across the headland above the burial mound so high that nothing could get over it except a bird in flight. Traces of it can still be seen. There Thórólf lay quietly as long as Arnkel was alive.

CHAPTER 35

Arnkel slays Hauk and takes possession of Snorri's timber.

SNORRI GODI had kept right on cutting wood in Krákuness Forest in spite of Thórólf Lamefoot's objections. But Arnkel godi let it be known that he regarded the transfer of ownership as illegal, and that Thórólf had defrauded him of his inheritance by selling the forest to Snorri.[1]

One summer Snorri sent his slaves to work the forest. They cut much timber,[2] piled it up, and then went home. While the wood was drying, Arnkel acted as though he were going to take the timber to his farm, but did nothing about it. However, he told his shepherd to be on the lookout and to tell him when Snorri was going to have the wood brought to his place. When the wood was dry, Snorri sent three of his slaves to fetch it. He sent Hauk, a henchman of his, along to protect them. They went there, loaded the timber on twelve horses, and set out for home.

Arnkel's shepherd caught sight of them then and informed Arnkel. He took his weapons and rode after them. He overtook them between Svelgsá River and Hólar. When he caught up with them, Hauk sprang from his horse and thrust at Arnkel with his spear. It struck his shield, and he was not wounded. Then Arnkel leaped from his horse and thrust his spear right through Hauk's middle, and he fell down dead at the place which is now called Hauksá River. And when the slaves saw that Hauk was killed, they took to their heels and ran for home. Arnkel chased them all the way beyond the Oxnabrekkur Hills. There he turned back and drove the horses home with him. He unloaded the wood and turned the horses loose after fastening on them the ropes [the wood had been tied with]. Then they were put on their way over

---

[1] In this Arnkel was right. According to Old Icelandic law it was illegal to dispose of property without the consent of the heirs. Arnkel could have brought suit to have his father outlawed for three years or deprived of the right to manage his property.

[2] Throughout the chapter, the word 'timber, wood for building' is used. It is most unlikely, however, that the small birch trees of Iceland could have been used for this purpose. Building wood had to be brought from Norway.

the mountain, and they continued on it till they reached Helgafell. These events became known. Everything remained quiet during that half year.

The following spring, however, Snorri godi prepared a charge of manslaughter against Arnkel for the killing of Hauk, while Arnkel demanded that Hauk be declared outlawed because of his attack on him. Both sides went with a large following to the Thórsness Assembly, and the cases were hotly contested. The case ended by the decision that Hauk had fallen outside the protection of the law because of his attack on Arnkel, and so Snorri's case fell to the ground. With that they rode home from the assembly. There was much suppressed enmity between the parties during the summer.

CHAPTER 36

Thorleif's attempt on Arnkel's life fails.

THORLEIF WAS THE NAME of a man from the East Fjords who had been outlawed for rape. He came to Helgafell that autumn and asked Snorri to take him in, but Snorri turned him away. They talked a great deal together before he left. Thorleif then went to Bólstead and arrived there in the evening and stayed for two nights. Arnkel got up early in the morning and began to nail together the outer door of his house. And when Thorleif arose, he went up to Arnkel and asked him to let him stay there. Arnkel would not hear of that and asked him whether he had been to see Snorri godi.

"I saw him all right," replied Thorleif, "and I asked him to let me stay with him; but he refused point-blank. For that matter," said Thorleif, "I am not especially keen about serving a man who always puts up with getting the worst of it, no matter who his opponent is."

"It doesn't strike me," said Arnkel, "that Snorri would be getting a bargain in you even if he gave you only your food in return for your services."

"Here is where I really want to stay," insisted Thorleif, "with a man like you."

"I am not in the habit of engaging men from outside the district," replied Arnkel.

They argued about the matter for a while, Thorleif sticking to his request and Arnkel refusing to accept him. Arnkel had laid aside his adze to bore holes in the cross plank of the door. Thorleif seized the axe and quickly swung it aloft, intending to brain Arnkel with it. But Arnkel heard the whiz and ran in under the blow. He seized Thorleif and lifted him onto his chest;[1] and it soon became apparent who was the stronger of the two, for Arnkel was a man of tremendous strength. He gave Thorleif such a fall that he was dazed and the axe flew from his hands. Arnkel snatched it up and struck Thorleif in the head with it and killed him. The rumor arose that Snorri godi had sent that man after Arnkel's head. Snorri didn't concern himself about this talk and let the people say what they wanted to. Thus another half year passed uneventfully.

---

[1]This is a trick in Icelandic wrestling to get an opponent off his feet.

CHAPTER 37

Arnkel's death at the hand of Snorri and the sons of Thorbrand.

THAT FALL, at the beginning of the winter season,[1] Snorri godi held a big autumn feast to which he invited his friends. Ale was served, and when the guests had become merry with the drink, they talked about the merits of men: who was the most outstanding man or the greatest chieftain in the district; and there was no agreement in the matter, as is

---

[1]Winter was reckoned to begin middle of October.

usually the case when people talk about the merits of different men.[2] Most of them thought that Snorri godi was the most distinguished man, but some mentioned Arnkel. Still others favored Styr.

While they were arguing about this, Thorleif Kimbi said, "Why are you men wrangling about this when all can clearly see how matters stand?"

"What do you mean by that, Thorleif?" they asked. "You are making a pretty bold assertion!"

"To me, Arnkel seems the most outstanding man by far," he said. "And what makes you think so?" they asked.

"Nothing but the facts," he replied. "I maintain that Snorri and Styr together only count as one man because of their relationship by marriage. No followers of Arnkel lie unatoned for by his place, whom Snorri has killed, as does Snorri's man Hauk, whom Arnkel killed."

That seemed bold speech to them, even though true, once they had gotten so far in their talk; and so they quit talking about it. But when the guests were leaving the banquet, Snorri picked out gifts for his friends. He conducted the sons of Thorbrand to their ship lying at the Raudavík Headland.

And when they parted, Snorri stepped up to Thorleif and said, "Here is an axe, Thorleif, which I want to give you. It has the longest handle of any axe I own, and yet it will not reach Arnkel's head as he is bringing in his hay at Orlygsstead if you brandish it from your place in Álptafirth."

Thorleif accepted the axe and said, "Don't think that I will hesitate to swing this axe at Arnkel once you are ready to avenge your follower Hauk."

Snorri replied, "I think you sons of Thorbrand owe it to me to be on the lookout for a chance to get at Arnkel, and you may hold me up to shame if I fail to join you once you have let me know when there is a chance to do so."

They parted, agreeing that they were all ready to put Arnkel out of the way and that the sons of Thorbrand should keep an eye on his movements.

Early that winter the fjords were frozen over. Freystein Bófi was herding sheep in Álptafirth. He had been stationed there to let his foster brothers know when there was a good chance to attack Arnkel.

---

[2] The matching or comparison of persons was a popular pastime in Scandinavian antiquity. Frequently it led to disputes and sometimes to serious trouble.

Arnkel was a hard worker and had his slaves work every day from sunrise to sunset. Arnkel managed the farms of Úlfarsfell and Orlygsstead, since no one else dared to for fear of the sons of Thorbrand. During the winter it was the custom of Arnkel to transport hay from Orlygsstead to his own farm on nights when the moon was nearly full, since the slaves were busy doing other work all day. Nor was he concerned whether or not the sons of Thorbrand could see him moving the hay. One night before Yule Arnkel got up during the night and waked three of his slaves, one of them by the name of Ófeig. Farmer Arnkel went to Orlygsstead with them; they took four oxen and two sleds along. The sons of Thorbrand became aware of this. Freystein Bófi immediately went along the frozen shore to Helgafell and arrived there after the people had been in bed for some time. He waked Snorri, and Snorri asked him what he wanted. He replied, "To his feed now has flown the old eagle, to Orlygsstead."

Snorri got up and told his men to get dressed. When they were dressed, they took their weapons and went, nine men strong, along the frozen shore to Álptafirth. And when they had reached the head of the fjord, the sons of Thorbrand joined them, six in all, and they went on up to Orlygsstead. And when they arrived there, the one slave had already gone back with a sled load of hay; and Arnkel and the other two were busy making up a second. Then they caught sight of armed men coming up from the sea. Ófeig said it looked like a fight— "and the only thing for us to do is to hurry home."

Arnkel replied, "I have a good plan: let each do what he considers best. You two run home and wake my men, and they will come at once to join me. There is a good vantage ground for defense here in the enclosure, and I can stand them off from here if these men mean to attack me. I consider that better than running away. They won't get the better of me so quickly, and my men will soon be here if you do well what I told you."

No sooner had Arnkel said that than the slaves took to their heels. Ófeig was the swifter of the two. He became so frightened that he nearly lost his wits. He ran up onto the mountain and jumped into a waterfall where he died. That place is now called Ófeig's Falls. The other slave ran home to the farm, and when he got there he found the first slave carrying in the hay. He called to the other who came running to help him carry in the hay; and it was clear that fellow did not mind work, for he pitched in right away.

Now to return to Arnkel. He recognized the men approaching as Snorri and his followers. He tore a runner from the sled and took it with him up into the enclosure. The outside wall of the enclosure was high, but the ground inside was filled up rather high so that it was a good place for defense. There was hay in the enclosure, but that nearest the wall had been removed. And when Snorri and his men arrived there, we are not told that any words were lost on either side. They made an assault on Arnkel immediately, thrusting at him with their spears; but Arnkel parried their thrusts with the sled runner and broke many a spear shaft. Arnkel was not wounded. When they had used up their missiles, Thorleif Kimbi ran up to the enclosure and leaped up on the wall with drawn sword. Arnkel struck at him with the sled runner, and Thorleif let himself fall backward to avoid the blow. The runner struck the wall where a piece of frozen turf stuck out and broke at the place where the strap holes were bored through it, and one piece flew outside the enclosure. Arnkel had leaned his sword and shield against the hay. He took up his weapons and defended himself with them, but now was in greater danger of being wounded. When his enemies had got up into the enclosure, Arnkel leaped up on the haystack and defended himself there for a while. But in the end Arnkel fell, and they covered his body with hay inside the enclosure.[3] After that Snorri and his men went home to Helgafell. Thormód Trefilsson composed this verse about the slaying of Arnkel:

26. Fame won him folk-lord,
    fighting, with victory:
    sated young Snorri
    slavering wolf-brood;
    the gladdener-of-ravens[4]
    gashed then the life-stack[5]
    with the flame-of-Fjolnir
    when he felled Arnketil.

Now to tell about the two slaves: they went into the house after having carried the hay in and took off their outer garments of leather.

---

[3]Though originally, of course, to protect the corpse from the ravages of beasts of prey, it was an unwritten law to cover up a foe slain in honorable combat.

[4]Kenning for 'warrior'.

[5]This curious kenning for 'ribs', reproduced from the original, carries out the figure implied in the 'flame-of-Fjolnir' for 'sword'.

At this Arnkel's followers woke up and asked where he was. Then it seemed as if the one slave woke up out of a sleep. "That's true," he said, "he is probably fighting with Snorri godi at Orlygsstead."

Then the men sprang up, got dressed, and hastened as quickly as possible to Orlygsstead where they found their master Arnkel dead. His death was lamented by all, for he was in every respect one of the best and wisest men in the ancient faith. He was composed, stouthearted, and as daring as anyone; determined, yet with a good hold on himself. He was generally successful in litigation with whomsoever he contended. It was for this reason that he provoked much jealousy, as was shown in this case. The body of Arnkel was now taken and brought to his burial place. Arnkel was placed in a mound by the sea near the Vadilshofdi Promontory, and that mound is as wide around as a large fenced-in haystack.[6]

---

[6]The last few sentences of this chapter, fulsomely eulogizing Arnkel, look like a later interpolation.

CHAPTER 38

Arnkel's widow does not obtain full redress.

AFTER THE SLAYING of Arnkel there were only women as heirs and chief prosecutors. Hence the prosecution was not pushed so vigorously as might have been expected for so prominent a man. Yet the parties came to an agreement in the matter. But the only sentence imposed was the lesser outlawry for Thorleif Kimbi, who was exiled for three years since the death wound of Arnkel was attributed to him. But as the outcome of this suit was not so honorable as befitted so great a chieftain as Arnkel, the leading men of the country had it enacted as law that never afterwards were women or youths under sixteen to be the chief prosecutors in cases of manslaughter; and this law has been observed ever since.[1]

---

[1]This is in agreement with the facts as stated in the codex *Grágás,* the oldest codification of Icelandic law.

CHAPTER 39

Thorleif and Arnbjorn's quarrel.

THAT SUMMER Thorleif Kimbi took passage with some merchants who were readying their ship in the Straum Firth, and he joined the skipper's mess. In those days it was the custom among merchants not to have a cook but to let the members of a mess decide by lot from day to day who of their number should do the cooking. But the entire crew got their drinking water from a water barrel which was fitted with a lid and stood by the mast. Additional drinking water was carried in casks, from which the water in the barrel was replenished as it was used.

And when they were almost ready to sail, a tall man with a pack on his back came to Búdarhamar, [the place near where the ship was moored]. He had a rather strange appearance. He asked for the skipper and was directed to his booth.[1] He laid down his bundle at the door and went in. He asked if the skipper would grant him passage across the ocean. They asked him what his name was, and he replied that he was Arnbjorn, the son of Ásbrand from Kamb. He said he wished to go abroad and look for his brother Bjorn, who had left Iceland a number of years before and had not been heard from since he sailed for Denmark. The Norwegians said that they had already secured their

---

[1]The 'booths' which are mentioned so frequently in the sagas were temporary shelters consisting of walls made of stones and turf over which a piece of sailcloth was placed during the time they were occupied.

cargo and did not think it wise to shift it again.[2] He said he had no more goods than could well lie on top of the cargo. And since it seemed urgent to them that he go, they took him on. He ate by himself and was assigned a place forward in the bow. In his bundle were 360 ells of wadmal,[3] twelve sheepskins, and his provisions for the voyage. Arnbjorn was handy at doing things and very willing to work, and so the merchants took a liking to him. They had an easy passage and came to Hordaland,[4] where they made fast at an outlying skerry.

They prepared their food on land there. It was Thorleif Kimbi's turn to do the cooking, and he was about to cook the porridge [for his mess]. Arnbjorn was on shore cooking his, and he was using the kettle which Thorleif was to use after him. Thorleif went ashore and asked Arnbjorn to let him have the kettle, but he was not done yet and was still stirring his porridge in the kettle. Thorleif stood over him. Then the Norwegians shouted from the ship that Thorleif should get on with the cooking and said that he certainly was a true Icelander from the way he was taking his time.[5] Then Thorleif lost his temper. He seized the kettle, dumped Arnbjorn's porridge on the ground, and turned to leave [with the kettle]. Arnbjorn was left holding the ladle. He struck at Thorleif with it and hit him in the neck. It was a light blow, but since the porridge was boiling hot, it burned Thorleif's neck.

He said, "We shan't let these Norwegians laugh at us two countrymen, that they have to separate us like fighting dogs; but I shall remember this when we two are in Iceland again."

Arnbjorn did not reply. They were there for several days before they had a favorable breeze to sail to the mainland and unload their cargo. Thorleif stayed in Norway, but Arnbjorn secured passage on the boat of some merchants and sailed with them to Vík and from there to Denmark to look for his brother Bjorn.

---

[2] The baggage was stowed away on deck and covered with cloth tied down over it.
[3] Wadmal was native homespun cloth.
[4] Province of western Norway.
[5] The Icelanders seem rather generally to have been regarded by the Norwegians as somewhat leisurely and slow in their movements.

CHAPTER 40

Bjorn resumes his dalliance with Thurid.

THORLEIF KIMBI remained in Norway for two years and then returned to Iceland with the same merchants with whom he had gone abroad. They sailed into the Broad Firth and landed at Dogurdarness. Thorleif went home to Álptafirth in the autumn and was quite pleased with himself, as was his custom.

That same summer the two brothers, Bjorn and Arnbjorn, came out to Iceland, landing at the mouth of the Hraunhaven Inlet. Bjorn was afterward called the Champion of the Breidavík people. Arnbjorn had brought good money with him; and as soon as he was back, he bought land at Bakki in Hraunhaven. Here he built a house the following spring. He spent the winter at Knorr with Thórd Blígr, his kinsman-in-law. Arnbjorn was not a showy person, and was reticent in most things, and yet he was an excellent man in every respect. His brother Bjorn cut quite a figure and had a grand bearing when he returned to Iceland, because he had patterned himself after the manner of foreign chieftains. He was far handsomer than Arnbjorn, but in nowise less of a man, but rather far more tested in valor since he had improved himself in foreign parts.

During the summer just after their return, a large and well-attended meeting had been called on the northern slope of the peninsula at a place called Haugabrekkur, a little east of the mouth of Fróðá Creek; and all the merchants [from the ship] rode there dressed in colored clothing.[1] When they arrived at the meeting, there were already many people there, including Thuríd, the mistress of Fróðá. Bjorn went to talk with her, and no one was surprised at that. They took it for granted that they would have much to talk about after not having seen each other for such a long time. At this meeting some men got into a fight, and one of the men from the northern shore was fatally wounded. He was carried under some bushes which stood on the point of land

---

[1]Clothing made of dyed (imported) cloth was worn only by wealthy or prominent people. Cf. Chap. 20, note 2.

there. Much blood ran from the wound, so that there was a pool of blood in the thicket. The boy Kjartan, the son of Thuríd of Fródá, was there and had a small axe in his hand. He ran to the bushes and dipped his axe into the blood. And when the men from the southern slope were riding homeward from the meeting, Thórd Blígr asked Bjorn what course the conversation with Thuríd had taken. Bjorn indicated that he was pleased with it. Then Thórd asked him whether he had seen the boy Kjartan during the day, the son of Thórodd among others.[2]

"Yes, I saw him," said Bjorn.

"And what do you think of him?" asked Thórd.

Then Bjorn spoke this verse:

27. A boy I saw in the bush, to
    burn-of-Fenrir[3] running,
    awful were his eyes[4]—not
    unlike to me was he;
    but hardly, say war-workers,
    would Thórodd's inheritor
    know the roller-steed's-ruler[5]
    really is his father.

Thórd asked, "What will Thórodd say now as to which of you is the boy's father?"

Then Bjorn spoke this verse:

28. For certain would the slender
    silver-Gefn[6] of Thórodd—
    the lady linen-dight did
    love me—confirm his inkling
    if the high-born head-dress-
    Hlín[6] had other offspring—
    e'er eager am I for the
    ash-of-gold[7]—who me resembled.

---

[2] A rather broad hint that Thórodd was not Kjartan's father. This is immediately confirmed by Bjorn.

[3] Fenrir is the mythologic great wolf; 'burn-of-Fenrir' hence, kenning for 'trickle-of-blood'.

[4] Keen flashing eyes were regarded as an indication of noble parentage.

[5] Ships were pulled up on shore for winter on rollers. Hence, 'roller-horse' is a kenning for 'ship'; the 'roller-steed's-ruler' here, Bjorn.

[6] Gefn and Hlín are minor goddesses. Hence, 'silver-Gefn' and 'head-dress-Hlín' are kennings for 'woman'; here, Thuríd.

[7] Cf. Chap. 28, note 3.

Thórd said, "And yet it would be best for you two not to see each other any more. Try to forget Thuríd, Bjorn."

"That is probably good advice," replied Bjorn, "and yet it is far from my mind, even though I am aware that her brother Snorri is superior to me in influence and power."

"Do as you think best," said Thórd.

And with that they broke off their conversation.

Bjorn now went home to Kamb and took over the management of the farm, since his father was dead. That winter he again took to crossing the mountains to pay his visits to Thuríd. But even though Thórodd objected to this, he thought it difficult to deal with the situation. He recalled how badly he had fared once before when he had complained of their relationship, and he saw that Bjorn was far more powerful now than formerly. During the winter Thórodd paid the witch Thorgríma Galdrakin to conjure up a snowstorm when Bjorn was to cross the mountains.

One day Bjorn again went to Fródá. In the evening when he was getting ready to go home, the weather was thick and rather rainy. It was quite late by the time Bjorn was ready to leave. And when he came up on the mountains, the weather turned cold, with drifting snow. By that time it was so dark that he could not see the path before him. Then the storm worsened, and there was such a gale that he could hardly keep his feet. His clothing was already soaking wet and now began to freeze on him. He became so confused that he did not know in which direction he was going. During the night he came to a small cave under an overhang. He crept into it and had cold quarters for the night. Then he spoke this verse:

29. Hardly would the Hlín-of-
hoarded-armrings—she who
her spouse's spacious couch doth
spread—think good my plight here
if the necklace-Njorun[8]
knew that I, the sea-steed's-
leader, now was lying
lonesome in cave and shivered.

---

[8]Njorun is a goddess; 'necklace-Njorun', a kenning for 'woman'.

And he again spoke a verse:

30. [9]Unfalteringly, my fraught ship
    furrowed the swan's-road's[10]
    icy waters—for she
    warmly loved me—from th' east:
    the helmsman much mishap
    whelmed; and now he lies
    cowering here in cold
    cave, instead of her bed.

Bjorn remained in the cave for three days before the storm abated. And then he came down from the mountains and reached his home at Kamb on the fourth day. He was quite exhausted. When the members of his household asked where he had been during the storm, Bjorn spoke this verse:

31. Unflinching, in wild fray I
    fought 'neath Styrbjorn's banner;
    helm-clad, hardy Eric[11]
    havoc wrought 'mong warriors:
    but now I erred on uplands,
    utterly lost, because I
    in the witch's wet snow-
    weather had lost my bearings.

Bjorn stayed at home the rest of the winter. In the spring his brother Arnbjorn established himself in Hraunhaven; but Bjorn remained at Kamb, where he lived in grand style.

---

[9]This verse is in a skaldic meter called *hálfhnept,* differing from the usual *dróttkvætt* measure chiefly in having each line end with an accented syllable.
[10]Kenning for 'sea'.
[11]King of Sweden, victor over Styrbjorn.

CHAPTER 41

The altercation between Thorleif and Thórd.

THAT SAME SPRING at the Thórsness Assembly Thorleif Kimbi made a proposal of marriage, asking for the hand of Helga Thorláksdóttir of Eyr, the sister of Steinthór of Eyr. He was supported most in this suit by her brother Thormód, who was married to Thorgerd Thorbrandsdóttir, the sister of Thorleif Kimbi. But when the matter was brought before Steinthór, he was rather reluctant to grant the request and to a certain measure left it to the decision of his brothers. They then went to Thórd Blígr.

And when this question was broached to him, he answered as follows: "So far as I am concerned, I shall not shift the responsibility of making a decision to others. I am man enough to do that myself. And so I declare to you, Thorleif, that first the porridge scars that were burned on your neck three years ago when you were beaten in Norway must be healed before I will give my sister to you in marriage."

Thorleif replied, "I do not know what luck I shall have in avenging this. But I could wish that three years won't pass before you get a beating."

Thórd replied, "I am not frightened by your threats."

The following morning there was a turf game[1] near the booth of the sons of Thorbrand. And as the sons of Thorlák walked by, a large piece of turf came flying through the air and struck Thórd Blígr on his neck. The force of the blow was so great that Thórd went down head over heels. And when he got up, he saw that the sons of Thorbrand roared with laughter at him. The sons of Thorlák turned about immediately, drawing their swords. Then the two parties ran to attack each other and right away came to blows. Several men were wounded, but none were killed. Steinthór had not been present, for he had been talking with Snorri godi. And when the two parties were separated, an attempt was made to bring about a settlement. It was agreed that Snorri and

---

[1]The turf game is mentioned only in this saga. Apparently it consisted in trying to hit a target with clods or pieces of turf.

Steinthór should make the decision. The wounds of the men and the act of starting the fight were weighed against each other, and the difference was paid in fines. And when they rode home, all the men were declared reconciled.

CHAPTER 42

The sons of Thorbrand attempt to slay Arnbjorn.

THAT SUMMER a ship landed at the entrance to the Hraunhaven Inlet, and another at Dogurdarness Peninsula. Snorri godi had some business with the ship at Hraunhaven, and so he rode from home with fourteen men. And when they had crossed the mountains southward into Dufgusdale, six heavily armed men came galloping after them. They were the sons of Thorbrand. Snorri asked them where they intended to go. They replied that they were going to the ship at Hraunhaven. Snorri said he would take care of their business there and asked them to go home and not start a fight. He said that often little was needed to start one if men who were already on bad terms happened to come upon one another.

Thorleif Kimbi replied, "People shall not say that we dared not ride about the district for fear of the Breidavík people. But you ride on home yourself if you are afraid to continue even though you have an errand."

Snorri did not reply.

They then rode across the ridges to Hofgardar and from there along the sandy beach. And when they had almost reached the inlet of Hraunhaven, the sons of Thorbrand left the group and headed for Bakki. When they arrived at the farmhouse, they sprang from their horses and tried to get into the house; but they were unable to break open the door. So they leaped onto the roof and began to break a hole in it. Arnbjorn took up his weapons and defended himself from the inside. He thrust at them through the thatch with his spear and inflicted wounds on them. This all happened early in the morning, and the weather was bright and clear.

That same morning the people of Breidavík had got up early to ride to the ship; and when they had come around the Oxl Promontory, they saw a man dressed in fine colored clothing on top of the roof at Bakki. They knew from his dress that it was not Arnbjorn. So Bjorn and his men turned and rode in that direction. But when Snorri godi discovered that the sons of Thorbrand had left his party, he rode after them. When he got to Bakki, they were trying furiously to break a hole in the roof. Snorri asked them to desist and not to commit any hostilities while they were members of his group. And since they had not succeeded in gaining entrance to the house, they gave up the attack, as Snorri had asked them to, and rode along with him to the ship.

The Breidavík people also came to the ship during the day, and everyone stayed close to his own group. There was much suppressed enmity between the two parties, and they were on their guard against each other, but neither made an attack upon the other. The men of Breidavík were more numerous than Snorri's band at the trading place. In the evening Snorri godi rode eastward to Hofgardar and spent the night there with Bjorn and his son Gest, the father of Hofgarda-Ref.[1] Bjorn the Champion of the Breidavik people and his men offered to Arnbjorn to ride after Snorri godi; but Arnbjorn did not want to, saying that each side should keep whatever advantage it had gained. Snorri and his men continued home the following day, and the sons of Thorbrand were now more dissatisfied with the way things had turned out than before. And now fall was drawing to a close.

---

[1]Hofgarda-Refr was a well-known skald.

CHAPTER 43

*The slave Egil is slain. The Breidvíkings bring the wergild for him to
the Álptafirth.*

FARMER THORBRAND in Álptafirth had a slave called Egil the Strong,
who was a very large and powerful man. He was dissatisfied with his
lot as a slave. He often begged Thorbrand and his sons to free him and
promised to do anything within his power in return. One evening Egil
was herding the sheep along the Álptafirth in the neighborhood of
Borgardale. As the evening was wearing on, he saw an eagle flying from
the west across the fjord. Egil had a large foxhound with him. The
eagle swooped down on the dog, seized him with its claws, and flew
westward back across the fjord with him to the mound of Thórólf
Lamefoot, where it disappeared on the other side of the mountain. Thorbrand said that this occurrence was probably a foreboding of great events
to come.

It was the custom of the people of Breidavík to hold ball games during
the first days of winter at the foot of the mountain Oxl south of Knorr
at a place which has since been called Leikskálavellir ('Play-shed
Fields'). Men from the entire district used to come there. Large shelter
huts for the players were built there. The men brought their provisions
along and stayed for two weeks or longer. At that time many excellent
people lived in the neighborhood and it was thickly populated. Most of
the younger men took part in the games, but not Thórd Blígr. He was
not permitted to be in the games—not so much because of his great
strength as because of his combativeness. He sat on a chair and
watched. Neither were the two brothers, Arnbjorn and Bjorn, because
of their great strength, considered suited to take part in the games, unless, indeed, they were matched against each other.

That same autumn the sons of Thorbrand told Egil that if he wished
to earn his freedom he should go to the ball games and kill one of the men
from Breidavík—Bjorn, or Thórd, or Arnbjorn—in some way or another. Some people say that this was done on the advice of Snorri
godi, and that he had laid down a plan for Egil to try to hide in one of the
sheds and to make his attack from there. He told him to come down from

the mountains by way of the gap above Leikskálar farm, and to do that when the meal-fires were lighted; for, as he said, the weather was such there that a sea breeze usually sprang up in the evening, which carried the smoke up through the gap. And he told him to wait and not come down through the gap until it was filled with smoke.

Egil started out on this venture. He first skirted the fjords, asking about the sheep belonging to the people of Álptafirth and pretending he was searching for them. Meanwhile Freystein Bófi was to keep the sheep by the Álptafirth. During the evening, after Egil had left, Freystein was tending the sheep west of the creek [which flows into the firth]. When he came to the landslide called Geirvor, which slopes down to the creek, he saw a man's head lying uncovered on the ground. The head spoke this ditty:

32. Reddened is Geirvor
     with the gore of men:
     haply she'll hide
     the heads of many.[1]

Freystein reported this portent to Thorbrand, who took it as foreboding dire events.

Now to tell of Egil: he came out past the fjords and then climbed up into the mountains this side of the Búland Headland and continued southward over the mountains, following a course which brought him to the gap above Leikskálar farm. There he hid during the day and watched the games below.

Thórd Blígr was sitting and watching the games. He said, "I don't know what it is I see up there in the gap. It may be a bird, or it may be a man hiding there and standing up from time to time. At any rate, it's something living. It seems to me that we should go and investigate." But that was not done.

On that day it was the turn of Bjorn the Breidavík Champion and Thórd Blígr to prepare the food. Bjorn was to tend the fire while Thórd went to fetch water. And when the fire was kindled, the smoke drifted up into the gap, as Snorri had guessed it would. Egil then came down under cover of the smoke and headed for the shed. The games were not yet over although it was quite late in the day. The fires blazed up high and filled the shed with smoke, and Egil made for it. He had grown

---

[1] The verse is to be interpreted as a foreboding that many will be slain and interred there—as is told in the following chapter.

quite stiff from lying up in the gap. He was wearing shoes with long tasseled laces, as was the fashion in those days, and one of them had become loose so that the tassel dragged on the ground. The slave entered the outer room. And when he came to enter the main hall, he tried to move quietly, for he saw that Bjorn and Thórd were sitting by the fire. Now Egil hoped in a brief moment to gain his freedom for life. But when he went to step over the threshold, he stepped with one foot on the tassel of the dragging shoelace. And when he tried to lift his other foot, the lace was fast, and he tripped and fell into the hall. He landed with such a thud that it sounded as though a flayed beef carcass had been flung down on the floor. Thórd jumped up and asked what kind of lubber that was. Bjorn also sprang up and grabbed him before he could get to his feet and asked him who he was.

He replied, "I am Egil, comrade Bjorn."

"Which Egil?" asked Bjorn.

"Egil from Álptafirth," he said.

Thórd drew his sword and wanted to strike him down. Bjorn held Thórd and told him not to be in such a hurry to kill the man—"we first want to get the truth from him." They then tied Egil's feet. In the evening, when the men returned to the shed, Egil related, so that all could hear, what the purpose of his errand had been. They let him sit there during the night, but in the morning they led him up into the gap—it is now called Egilsskard ('Egil's Gap')—and slew him there.[2]

In those days it was the law that if a man killed someone else's slave, he was to deliver payment for that slave's life to his owner's residence, and that he was to set out to do so within three days after the slaying. And the amount was fixed at twelve ounces of silver. If so delivered, there was no cause for prosecution. After the killing of Egil, the men of Breidavík decided to deliver the payment for him according to the law. They carefully chose a band of thirty men from those at Leikskálar. They rode north across the mountains and spent the night at Eyr[3] with Steinthór. He joined them, so that now there were sixty men in the troop. They skirted the heads of the fjords and spent the second night at Bakki with Steinthór's brother Thormód. They called on their kinsmen, Styr and Vermund, to join them, and now there were eighty all together.

---

[2]According to an unwritten law (*Náttvíg eru morðvíg* 'night slayings are the same as murder'), no executions were to take place the same day the crime was committed. This gave time to cool off if a decision was made in anger.

[3]This is the estate of Ondurd-Eyr, not to be confused with the Eyr east of Helgafell.

Then Steinthór sent a man to Helgafell to find out what plan Snorri godi would adopt if he learned of this gathering of armed men. But when this man came to Helgafell, he found Snorri godi sitting in his high seat, and there were no signs of any move on his part. The scout got no information of what Snorri's plans were. When he returned to Bakki, he told Steinthór what he had found out at Helgafell.

Steinthór said, "It was to be expected that Snorri would not interfere with our acting according to the law. And if he doesn't move in to Álptafirth, I see no reason why we should need this great host of men. I wish that we go about this matter quietly if we carry it out according to the law. It seems advisable to me, kinsman Thórd," he said, "that you Breidavík men remain here, because the thing we want least of all is to have you and the sons of Thorbrand get into a fight."

Thórd replied, "One thing is certain, and that is that I will go along. I shall not give Thorleif Kimbi a chance to jeer at me and say I was afraid to deliver the payment for the slave!"

Then Steinthór spoke to the brothers, Bjorn and Arnbjorn. "I wish," he said, "that you two would remain here with twenty men."

Bjorn replied, "I will not force myself on you if you do not think it proper for me to go along. But this is the first time I have ever been rejected by any company. I have a feeling," he added, "that Snorri is too clever for you. I cannot foresee the future, but I have a premonition that before we meet again things will have taken such a turn that your band will not seem any too large to you."

Steinthór said, "I shall make the plans for us as long as I am here, even if I am not so clever as Snorri godi."

"You may do so, kinsman, so far as I am concerned," replied Bjorn.

After that Steinthór rode away from Bakki with his band of nearly sixty men. They went in over Skeid to Drápuhlíd, and then over the Vatnsháls Ridge and across Svelgsárdale, and from there they headed toward Úlfarsfell Ridge.

CHAPTER 44

The battle by the Álptafirth.

SNORRI GODI had sent instructions to his neighbors to move their ships in under the protection of the Raudavík Headland, and he hurried there with his followers as soon as the man sent by Steinthór had left. He did not leave his place sooner than this because he assumed that this man had probably been sent to spy on his doings. Snorri entered the Álptafirth with three ships and nearly fifty men, and he arrived at Kárs-stead before Steinthór. And when Steinthór and his followers were seen approaching Kársstead, the sons of Thorbrand proposed that they should move out against them and prevent them from reaching the homefield—"since we have such a fine large band of men." There were eighty of them.

Then Snorri made this answer: "We must not prevent them from approaching the farm, and Steinthór must be allowed to proceed according to the law, for he will execute his business wisely and quietly. I want all you men to remain inside and not bandy words with them, as that will only stir up more trouble."

Thereupon all of them went inside and sat down on benches, but the sons of Thorbrand paced up and down the floor. Steinthór and his men rode up to the door. It is reported that he was wearing a red kirtle, with the front corners tucked up under his belt.[1] He had a beautiful shield and helmet and was girded with an exquisitely inlaid sword. The hilt was white with silver, and the haft wound with silver and edged with gold. Steinthór and his men dismounted, walked up to the door, and fastened a purse containing twelve ounces of silver to it.[2] He then named witnesses to the fact that the indemnity for the slave had been delivered according to law.

The door was open, and a serving woman standing in the doorway heard the naming of the witnesses. She went into the room and said,

---

[1]The long cloaks were slit in such a way that the corners could be turned and tucked under the belt for comfort and mobility.

[2]Literally, to the door groove. Sliding doors which moved vertically were common in Iceland till recent times.

"Steinthór of Eyr is not only a brave man; he also spoke well when he delivered the payment for the slave."

When Thorleif Kimbi heard that, he ran to the door, and the other sons of Thorbrand with him; and then all the men in the room made for the door. Thorleif was the first one outside. He saw Thórd Blígr standing before the door with his shield while Steinthór was just reaching the homefield. Thorleif seized a spear, which was standing in the doorway, and thrust at Thórd Blígr with it. It struck the shield and glanced off into the shoulder, inflicting a great wound. Now all the men came running out, and a battle started right in the homefield. Steinthór was the fiercest of all, swinging his sword to the right and to the left. When Snorri came out, he called on the men to stop fighting. He promised Steinthór not to pursue him if he would leave. Steinthór and his men rode away over the field, and thus the battle was broken off. But when Snorri came back to the house, he found his son Thórodd standing there with a large wound in his shoulder. He was then twelve years old. Snorri asked him who had wounded him.

"Steinthór of Eyr," he replied.

Thorleif Kimbi said, "Now he has repaid you properly for not wanting to pursue him. My advice is that we don't let bygones be bygones."

"Nor shall we," said Snorri; "our business with them isn't finished yet." And he told Thorleif to let the men know that they were to pursue them.

Steinthór and his men had just left the homefield when they caught sight of the men pursuing them. They rode across the river and turned up onto the landslide called Geirvor and made ready to fight there. That was a good place for defense because of the stones. And as Snorri's band was coming up there, Steinthór hurled a spear over them for good luck, following the old custom.[3] The spear sought its mark, and that was Snorri's kinsman Már Hallvardsson, who was disabled immediately.

When Snorri was told about this, he said, "It is a good thing that the adage proves true, that it isn't always safest to be in the rear."

Then a fierce battle began. Steinthór was at the head of his band and wielded his sword with both hands. But that beautifully ornamented sword failed him when it struck the shields, and he often had to straighten it under his foot. He sought out Snorri godi for his attack. Styr Thor-

---

[3]The pagan custom of beginning a battle by hurling a spear into the opposing host was attributed to Odin (cf. the Eddic poem *Völuspá*, stanza 24).

grímsson fought fiercely beside his kinsman Steinthór. He first killed a man from the band of Snorri, his son-in-law.

When Snorri saw that, he called out, "So that is how you avenge your daughter's son Thórodd, whom Steinthór almost killed. Scoundrel that you are!"

Styr replied, "I'll soon make up for that!" He then turned his shield, joining the company of Snorri, and killed a man from Steinthór's band.

Just then Áslák from Longdale and his son Illugi the Strong arrived and attempted to part them. They had thirty men in their company, and Vermund the Slender also joined them. They asked Snorri to put a stop to the killing. Snorri offered the men of Eyr a truce. Then they, on their part, asked Steinthór to accept a truce on behalf of them. Steinthór asked Snorri to extend his hand and he did so. Then Steinthór raised his sword and struck at Snorri's arm so that there was a sharp crack.[4] The blow had struck the altar ring and cut it almost in two, but Snorri was not wounded.

Then Thórodd Thorbrandsson called out, "They will keep no truce. Let us not stop the fight until all the sons of Thorlák are slain."

Snorri replied, "There would be no end of violence in the district if all the sons of Thorlák were slain. If Steinthór is willing, we will keep the truce on the terms already agreed upon."

Then they all asked Steinthór to accept this truce. And so an armistice was agreed to, which should be in effect until each one of the men reached his home.

Meanwhile the Breidavík people learned that Snorri had set out for Álptafirth with a large body of men. They mounted their horses and rode after Steinthór as swiftly as possible. They reached Úlfarsfell Ridge just as the battle was being fought on the landslide. Some people say that Snorri caught sight of Bjorn and his men as they were coming over the crest of the ridge and that that was why he was so willing to come to a truce with Steinthór.

Steinthór and Bjorn met at Orlygsstead. Bjorn said that things had gone just as he had surmised. "My advice is to turn back now and attack them hard."

Steinthór replied, "I will keep this truce with Snorri—however things may turn out between us later."

---

[4] It is to be kept in mind that Steinthór had not yet accepted the agreement. For that matter, this treacherous blow may be taken as Steinthór's answer to Snorri's having broken his promise not to pursue them.

Then they all rode home except Thórd Blígr, who had to stay at Eyr because of his wounds. In the battle in the Álptafirth five of Steinthór's men and two of Snorri godi's were killed, and many were wounded on each side since the fighting was extremely fierce. Thus says Thormód Trefilsson in the *Hrafnsmál*:[5]

33. Sated in sword-play
     the snake-of-wounds wielder[6]
     eagles on wolf's-food
     by the Álptafirth's shore.
     There and then Snorri
     in thing-of-arrows[7]
     felled five stout warriors:
     thus should foemen be punished.

Thorbrand had had a hand, along with Áslák and Illugi, in trying to stop the battle; and it was he who had asked them to try to bring about a reconciliation. He thanked both them and Snorri for their support. After the fight Snorri returned home to Helgafell. It was decided that the sons of Thorbrand should be alternately at Helgafell and at home in the Álptafirth until this feud was settled; for the suppressed enmity was very great, as was to be expected, since the truce came to an end as soon as the men got home.

[5] Cf. note on stanza 26.
[6] 'Snake-of-wounds' is a kenning for 'sword'.
[7] Kenning for 'battle'.

CHAPTER 45

The battle on the Vigrafjord.—Snorri heals the sons of Thorbrand.

THAT SAME SUMMER, before the battle in the Álptafirth, a ship had landed at Dogurdarness Peninsula, as has already been mentioned. There

Steinthór of Eyr had bought a good ten-oared boat, that had come with the ship. But when he tried to take his boat home, he was caught by a strong storm from the west which drove them eastward around Thórsness. So they landed at Thingskálaness and beached the boat at Gruflunaust. Then they walked across the ridges to Bakki and from there went home to Eyr by boat. Steinthór did not retrieve his own boat during the fall, and so it remained in the Grufla boatshed.

One morning shortly before Yule Steinthór got up early and said that he wanted to go in to Thingskálaness to fetch his boat. His brothers, Bergthór and Thórd Blígr, got ready to go with him. By now Thórd's wounds were quite healed so that he could bear arms again. Two of Steinthór's Norwegian guests also went along. In all there were eight. They were taken eastward across the fjord to the Selja Headland, from where they continued on foot to Bakki. Here they were joined by their brother Thormód, who made the ninth man in their party.

A heavy formation of ice covered Hofstadavág Bay almost to Bakki inn Meiri. They went eastward across the ice and then across the neck of land to the Vigrafjord, which was also completely frozen over. The nature of this inlet is such that at ebb tide it becomes completely dry and the ice settles down upon the mud flats. Then the skerries in the inlet project up through the ice. There was much broken ice around one skerry, and smooth blocks of ice slanted out from it to all sides. There had been a fall of light, dry snow, so that the ice was very slippery.

Steinthór and his men walked to Thingskálaness and pulled the boat out of the shed. They took the oars and board partitions out of the boat and laid them on the ice together with their clothing and heaviest weapons. Then they dragged the boat across the fjord, and then over the neck of land to Hofstadavág Bay, and all the way to open water. Then they started back for their clothing and other things. And when they got back to the Vigrafjord, they saw six men moving rapidly from the south from Thingskálaness across the ice in the direction of Helgafell. Steinthór and his men had a suspicion that these men were probably the sons of Thorbrand on their way to spend Yule at Helgafell. So they began to run east along the fjord to get their clothing and weapons, which they had left there. The others were the sons of Thorbrand, just as Steinthór had guessed. And when they caught sight of men running east along the frozen fjord, they took it for granted that these must be the men of Eyr and that they wanted to start a fight with them. They also began to run and headed for the skerry, intending to defend themselves there. Thus both parties were running directly toward each other, and the sons of Thorbrand reached the skerry first. When Steinthór and his men came alongside the skerry, Thorleif Kimbi hurled a spear into their band; and it struck Bergthór Thorláksson in the middle of the body, and he was put out of the fight immediately. He walked away a short distance and lay down on the ice. Some of Steinthór's men attacked the skerry while the others ran for their weapons. The sons of Thorbrand defended themselves well and bravely. Also, they had a good place for defence since the slabs of ice slanted steeply away from the skerry and were extremely slippery. And so no one of them was wounded until the men returned with the weapons. Then Steinthór and five others made a rush at the skerry while the two Norwegians withdrew to shooting distance to shoot with their bows and arrows. So now the men on the skerry suffered some wounds.

When Thorleif Kimbi saw Steinthór draw his sword, he called out, "You still wield your silverhilted sword, Steinthór! But I don't know whether it still has the soft blade it had this fall in the Álptafjord."

Steinthór answered, "You will find that out before the day is over whether or not my blade is soft."

The attack on the skerry was not successful at first. And after they had been skirmishing for quite some time, Thórd Blígr made a dash at the skerry and tried to thrust Thorleif Kimbi through with his spear, since he always was out in front of his band. The spear struck Thorleif's shield. But since Thórd had lunged too hard, his feet flew out from under him on the sloping cake of ice. He fell over backwards and slid head foremost down away from the skerry. Thorleif Kimbi rushed after him to inflict the deathblow on him before he could regain his feet. Freystein closely followed Thorleif. He had ice spurs on his shoes. Steinthór ran forward and held his shield over Thórd just as Thorleif struck at him. With his other hand he slashed at Thorleif and cut off his leg below the knee. At this moment Freystein Bófi thrust with his spear at Steinthór's middle. But Steinthór saw it and leaped up high so that the spear ran between his legs. And these three things he did at one and the same time, just as it is recounted here. Then he struck Freystein on the neck with his sword so that there was a loud crack.

Steinthór said: "Did that biff you, Bófi?"

"Biff it did," replied Freystein, "but not so badly as you wanted, because I am not wounded."

He was wearing a felt hood, into the neck piece of which a piece of horn was sewn, and the blow had struck this.

Then Freystein wheeled and ran back up on the skerry. Steinthór called out to him not to turn tail if he was not wounded. Thereupon Freystein veered around again on the skerry, and they fell upon each other most fiercely. Steinthór almost lost his footing on the steep, slippery slabs of ice, whereas Freystein stood firmly on his ice spurs and rained blows at him both fast and hard. But in the end Steinthór caught Freystein above the hips with a blow of his sword and cut him in half. After that they gained the top of the skerry and did not stop fighting until all the sons of Thorbrand had fallen. Thórd Blígr was for cutting off the heads of all the sons of Thorbrand, but Steinthór would not hear of putting to death fallen men. They then came down from the skerry and went to look for Bergthór. He was still able to speak, and they brought him to firm land from the ice and took him over the neck of land to their boat. Then they rowed to Bakki that same evening.

During the day one of Snorri godi's shepherds had been up on the Oxnabrekkur Hills overlooking the Vigrafjord and had watched the fight from there. He hurried home and told Snorri that a fierce clash had occurred on the Vigrafjord. Snorri and eight of his men took their weapons and hurried out to the fjord. By the time they arrived there, Steinthór and his men had already left the ice of the fjord and were gone. Snorri and his men examined the fallen and found that no one was dead except Freystein Bófi, but that all the others were seriously wounded. Thorleif Kimbi wanted Snorri to pursue Steinthór and his men and not to let any of them escape alive. Snorri walked over to a large clot of blood at the place where Bergthór had lain. He took up blood and snow together and squeezed it in his hand and put some in his mouth. He asked whose blood it was. Thorleif Kimbi said it was Bergthór's blood. Snorri said that the blood had come from inside the body.

"That may well be," replied Thorleif, "because he was felled by a spear hurled at him."

"I think," said Snorri, "that this is the blood of a man certain to die. There is no need to pursue them."

Then the sons of Thorbrand were brought to Helgafell, and their wounds were bandaged there. Thórodd Thorbrandsson had such a great wound on the back of his neck that he could not hold his head up. He was wearing trousers and stockings in one piece, and this garment was all soaked with blood. One of Snorri's men servants was to take it off. But when he pulled at the trousers, they would not come off.

Then he said, "It is no lie that you sons of Thorbrand like to be showy with your clothes, seeing you have garments so tight fitting that they won't come off."

Thórodd said, "Maybe you are not doing it the right way."

Then the man braced his one foot against the footboard of the bed and pulled with all his might, but he could not get the trousers off. Then Snorri came over to him and felt the leg and found that a spear point had gone between the knee tendon and the leg bone. Snorri said that the man certainly was a blundering fool not to have thought of a thing like that.

Snorri Thorbrandsson was the least incapacitated of the brothers. He sat at table beside his namesake. They had skyr[1] and cheese for supper that night. Snorri godi noticed that he was not eating much cheese and asked him why he was eating so slowly. Snorri Thorbrandsson replied that lambs ate least right after they had been gagged.[2] Then Snorri godi felt his throat and discovered an arrowhead lodged there crosswise at the base of the tongue. He took pincers and pulled it out, and after that Snorri Thorbrandsson was able to eat.

Snorri godi healed all the sons of Thorbrand. When Thórodd's neck began to heal, his head drooped forward somewhat. Then Thórodd said that Snorri wanted to heal him to be a cripple, but Snorri said he thought the head would straighten up when the sinews knit. Thórodd insisted that the wound be torn open again and the head set straighter. But Snorri turned out to be right. When the tendons grew together, the head straightened up, and he was able to bend it down but little afterward. Thorleif Kimbi always walked with a wooden leg thereafter.

---

[1]*Skyr*, the national dish of Iceland, is a milk food not unlike yogurt. It is usually eaten with sugar and cream. Many Icelanders attribute the sturdy good health of their children to this nutritious food.

[2]Sticks were sometimes fastened in the mouths of the lambs as an aid to weaning them. The technical term for this is 'gagging'.

CHAPTER 46

Peace is made between the Eyr dwellers and the Thórsnessings.

WHEN STEINTHÓR of Eyr and his men reached Bakki, they pulled the boat into the boatshed, and then the two brothers went up to the farm. Bergthór meanwhile was taken care of in the boatshed for the night. We are told that Thorgerd refused to go to bed with her husband Thormód that evening.[1] Just then a man came up from the boatshed with the news that Bergthór was dead. And when she heard that, Thorgerd got into her husband's bed, nor are we told that the two were at odds about this matter since then. Steinthór went home to Eyr the next morning, and the winter passed without any further acts of violence.

But in the spring, when the time for summoning approached, it seemed to men of good will that things had come to an evil pass in that the persons most highly regarded in the district had not become reconciled and were engaged in strife with each other. They chose the best men from among themselves, friends of either side, to try to bring about a reconciliation between them. Vermund the Slender was the leader of this group, among whom were many men of good will who were related by marriage to both parties. Finally a truce was arranged, and then a settlement was arrived at. Most people say that the decisions in the matter were left to Vermund. And he announced these decisions, come by with the help of the wisest men there, at the Thórsness Assembly; to wit, that the deaths and acts of aggression be weighed off against each other. The wound of Thórd Blígr, received in the Álptafirth, and the wound of Thórodd, the son of Snorri godi, balanced each other. The wound Már Hallvardsson had received and the blow Steinthór dealt Snorri godi offset the slaying of the three men who fell in the battle in the Álptafirth. The two slayings by Styr—one on each side—canceled each other. The killing of Bergthór in the Vigrafjord fight was of equal weight with the wounding of three of the sons of Thorbrand, while the

---

[1]Thorgerd, being the sister of the wounded Thorbrandssons and the half-sister of the slain Freystein Bófi, is reconciled with her husband only after the death of Bergthór has at least partly avenged the death and injuries of her relatives.

death of Freystein Bófi was regarded as of equal importance with the death of a man, not named above, who was killed by Steinthór in the Álptafirth battle. Thorleif Kimbi was paid compensation for the loss of his leg. The death of one of Snorri's men in the Álptafirth was off-set by the fact that Thorleif Kimbi had started the attack which re-sulted in this battle. Then the wounds of the other men were weighed off against each other, and whatever difference there seemed to be was settled by money payments. Thus the men rode home reconciled from the assembly, and this settlement was well kept as long as both Steinthór and Snorri lived.

CHAPTER 47

Snorri's attempt on Bjorn's life.

IN THE SAME SUMMER following this settlement Thórodd Skattkaupandi invited Snorri godi, his brother-in-law, to visit him at Fródá. Snorri went there with eight men. While Snorri was there, Thórodd com-plained to him that he felt he was being shamed and vexed by Bjorn Ásbrandsson, who was in the habit of coming there to talk to Thuríd, his wife and Snorri's sister. Thórodd said he thought it was Snorri's concern to seek redress for this aggravation. Snorri stayed there for several days; and when he left, Thórodd saw him on his way and gave him seemly gifts. From there Snorri rode south across the mountains and let it be known that he intended to ride to the ship laid up at the mouth of the Hraunhaven Inlet. It was summer, during the time of haymaking in the homefields.

But when they arrived on the height of Kamb Mountain, Snorri said, "From here we shall ride down in the direction of Kamb farm. I want you to know that I intend to make an attack on Bjorn and kill him if chances are favorable. But we will not attack him if he is inside, because

the buildings there are very strongly constructed, and Bjorn is a brave
and hardy fellow. Also, we don't have much of a force. People have
had little success attacking men of such prowess in their homes with
much larger forces than we have, as the example of Geir godi and
Gizur the White shows. With eighty men[1] they made an attack on
Gunnar in his house at Hlídarendi when he was alone to defend it.
Some were killed and some wounded, and they were about to give up
the attack when Geir godi discovered that Gunnar had run out of arrows. Now in case," Snorri continued, "Bjorn should be outside, as is
to be expected since this is such good drying weather, I want you, kinsman Már, to make an attack on him. But be on your guard, for he is
not a chickenhearted man. 'From warlike wolf I wait me strife'[2] if he is
not fatally wounded at the first onset."

And when they rode down from the mountains toward the farm, they
saw Bjorn on the homefield working on a hay-sledge. He was alone
and had no weapons except a small axe and a large whittling knife with
which he had cleaned the wood out of the bore holes. The blade was a
span in length from the haft. Bjorn saw Snorri and his men riding down
from the mountains and on to the plain, and he recognized them at once.
Snorri godi was dressed in a blue hooded cloak and was riding at the
head of his group. Bjorn made a quick decision: he grabbed the knife
and went toward them. As soon as he came up to Snorri, he seized the
sleeve of his cloak with his one hand, and with the other hand he held
the knife poised in such a way that he could most easily thrust it into
Snorri's chest if that were called for. Bjorn greeted them when they
met, and Snorri returned his greeting; but Már faltered because he
thought Bjorn would quickly stab Snorri if any attempt were made
to attack him. Then Bjorn went along with Snorri and his men and
asked what the common news was, at the same time keeping a firm
grip on Snorri's sleeve.

Then Bjorn spoke as follows: "The fact is, farmer Snorri, and I do
not deny it, that I have done some things to you which you can in justice
blame me for; and I have been told that you have been harboring
a grudge against me. Now it may be that you just happen to be riding

---

[1]While this is an exaggeration according to the *Njáls saga,* we must take into
account that Snorri is trying to impress his companions with the difficulty of such
an operation. Also, according to the *Njáls saga,* it is not Geir but Gizur who
suspected that Gunnar was running short of arrows.

[2]A quotation from the Eddic *Lay of Regin,* stanza 13, occurring also in *Laxdæla
saga,* Chap. 19.

by. But in case you have some business with me, I think you had better come out with it; and if so, I want you to grant me a truce, and I'll turn back, for I am not a fool to be led by the nose."

Snorri replied, "You got such a lucky grip on me when we met that we'll have to grant you a truce for the time being, regardless of what our intentions were. But this I want to ask of you, that you refrain henceforth from beguiling my sister Thuríd. For you and I can never be on peaceful terms if you go on doing what you have done in the past."

Bjorn answered, "I will promise only what I can keep, but I do not know how I can do that if Thuríd and I live in the same district."

Snorri replied, "There is really nothing to prevent you from moving away from this district."

Bjorn said, "What you say is true, and it shall be thus since you yourself have come to see me. The way our meeting has turned out, I will promise you that you and Thórodd will not be provoked during the next years by my visiting Thuríd."

"That would be doing the right thing," said Snorri.

After that they parted. Snorri godi rode to the ship and then home to Helgafell. On the following day Bjorn rode south to Hraunhaven and right away took passage on the ship there. They were late in getting started, and then they got a northeast wind which persisted for a long time during the summer. Nothing was heard of this ship for a long time afterward.

CHAPTER 48

Thorleif and Snorri Thorbrandsson emigrate to Greenland.

AFTER THE RECONCILIATION between the men of Eyr and those of Álptafirth, Snorri Thorbrandsson and Thorleif Kimbi sailed to Greenland. Thorleif lived there until old age; Kimbaság Bay between the glaciers is named for him. But Snorri sailed to Vínland the Good with Karlsefni. Snorri Thorbrandsson was one of the bravest of men. He was killed there in Vínland in a fight with the Skrælings.[1] Thórodd Thorbrandsson remained living in the Álptafirth. He was married to Ragnhild, the daughter of Thórd, the son of Thorgils Eagle, who was the son of Hallstein godi, who owned the slaves.[2]

---

[1]This does not agree with the saga of Eirík the Red, which states that Thorbrand Snorrason (not Snorri Thorbrandsson) was killed by the Skrælings (Indians) in Vínland.

[2]Apparently the incident alluded to here was well known in the 13th century since there are at least three other references to it in contemporary Icelandic literature. According to later folk tradition Hallstein, coming upon his slaves asleep when they were supposed to be making salt, hanged them by some cliffs called Gálgi ('Gallows').

CHAPTER 49

Christianity comes to Iceland.

THE NEXT EVENT reported is the coming of Gizur the White and his son-in-law Hjalti to Iceland to preach the gospel. Everybody was baptized, and Christianity was accepted as the law at the Althing.[1] Of all those from the Western Fjords, Snorri did most to have Christianity adopted. As soon as the assembly came to an end, Snorri had a church built at Helgafell; and Styr, his father-in-law, had another one built at his farm below Hraun. A great incentive toward the building of churches was that the priests promised that a person would provide room in the Kingdom of Heaven for as many as could find standing room in the church he built. Thórodd Skattkaupandi also had a church

---

[1]Cf. Chap. 24, note 1.

built on his farm at Fródá. But even after the churches had been built, there were no priests to hold services since there were few of them in Iceland at that time.

CHAPTER 50

Thorgunna's arrival in Iceland.

DURING THE SUMMER in which Christianity was made the law in Iceland, a ship came off the high seas and landed at Snæfellsness. It was a ship from Dublin. There were Irishmen and men from the Hebrides on it, also a few Norwegians. They lay under the lee of the ledge called Rif for a long time during the summer, waiting for a breeze to sail across the fjord to Dogurdarness, and many came from around the peninsula to trade with them.

On board was a Hebridean woman named Thorgunna.[1] Members of the crew said that she had brought some valuable things along such as were not easily obtained in Iceland. And when Thuríd, the housewife at Fródá, heard that, she was very curious to see these costly things; for she was quite fond of finery and much given to vain display. So she went to the ship to see Thorgunna and asked her if she had any women's attire of unusual quality. Thorgunna said her things were not for sale, but admitted that she possessed such clothing as she need not be ashamed to be seen in at festivals or other gatherings. Thuríd asked to see these things and was permitted to do so. They pleased her very much, for they were excellently made, yet not costly. Thuríd asked Thorgunna to sell them to her, but she refused. Then Thuríd invited her to take lodging at her place, for she knew that Thorgunna

---

[1] Attempts have been made to identify this Thorgunna with a highborn Hebridean woman of the same name with whom Leif Eiríksson had a liaison.

liked to dress up, and she thought she would be able to get the lovely things away from her by and by.

Thorgunna replied, "I accept your offer of lodging with pleasure, but I want you to know that I do not care to pay much for it since I am quite able to work. I don't mind working, but I will not do any hard labor. And I will determine myself how much of my money I will pay out for my lodging."

Even though Thorgunna spoke rather harshly, Thuríd insisted that she come along home with her. So her belongings were brought from the ship. She had a large locked chest and a smaller portable one. These things were transported to Fródá. And when Thorgunna arrived there, she asked to be shown her bed. A bed was assigned to her in the sleeping-hall at some distance from the door.[2] She unlocked the chest and took out her bedclothes, which were all elaborately worked. Over her bed she spread a fine English sheet and a silk counterpane. She also took from the chest bed curtains and the trimmings that belonged to them. They were such fine bed furnishings that the people thought they had never seen anything like them before.

Then mistress Thuríd said, "Make me a price on the bed furnishings."

Thorgunna replied, "I will not sleep on straw for your sake even though you are elegant and put on airs."

That angered Thuríd, and she did not again insist that she sell her the things.

Thorgunna worked at making cloth every day when there was no haying. But when there was good drying weather, she worked at drying the hay in the homefield. She had a rake made which she did not want anyone else to use.

Thorgunna was a large woman. She was tall and stout and well fleshed. Her eyebrows were dark and her eyes close-set. Her hair was brown and thick. She was generally of a good disposition and went to church every day before going to her work, but she was not easy-tempered or talkative for the most part. It was the opinion of the people that Thorgunna was probably in her fifties; yet she was still a most vigorous woman. At that time Thórir Woodenleg had come to Fródá for maintenance, and also his wife Thorgríma Galdrakin. They and Thorgunna could not get along with each other. Kjartan, the farmer's son, was the one person with whom Thorgunna most wished to deal; and she loved him very much. But he was rather cool toward her, and for that

---

[2] Naturally the beds nearest the door were the least desirable.

reason she was often irritable. Kjartan was then thirteen or fourteen years old, and he was both large and personable.

CHAPTER 51

The Fróðá marvels.

THE SUMMER was rather wet, but during the autumn there came some good days for drying. The haymaking at Fróðá had progressed to the extent that the entire homefield had been cut and almost half of the hay completely dried. Then there came a good drying day with calm, bright weather, so that there was not a single cloud to be seen in the sky. Farmer Thórodd got up early in the morning and assigned the work for the day. Some began bringing in the hay and others stacked it, but the women were assigned to dry the hay, and it was so arranged that Thorgunna was to toss and dry the cattle fodder.[1] And the work progressed well during the day.

But early in the afternoon a small black cloud appeared in the sky to the north above Skor.[2] It moved quickly across the sky straight for the farm. The people thought it would bring rain. Thórodd asked his hands to rake the hay together, but Thorgunna continued turning the hay most vigorously. She did not begin to rake it up even though she had been told to. The small cloud approached rapidly. And when it reached the farm at Fróðá, it was accompanied by such great darkness that the people could not see beyond the homefield and could scarcely make out their hands before their eyes. From this cloud came such a heavy rain that all the hay which was still lying flat was drenched. The cloud

---

[1] Because of the wet climate of Iceland it is often necessary to toss and turn the hay repeatedly in order to get it sufficiently dry to keep without rotting or moulding.

[2] A headland about forty miles directly north of Fróðá across the Broad Firth.

quickly passed over and the weather cleared up. Then people saw that it had rained blood.[3] During the evening the weather again became good for drying the hay, and the blood quickly dried on all the hay except where Thorgunna had been working. There the blood did not dry, nor did it ever dry on the rake she had been using.

Thórodd asked Thorgunna what she thought this strange occurrence might signify. She said she did not know—"but it seems most likely to me," she replied, "that it forebodes the death of someone here."

Thorgunna went home in the evening. She went to her bed, took off her bloody clothing, and lay down. She sighed heavily. And people then saw that she had taken sick. This shower had come nowhere except to Fródá. Thorgunna would not take any food that evening. And in the morning farmer Thórodd came to her and asked about her sickness and how she thought it would end. She replied that she thought this would be her last sickness.

Then she said, "I consider you the wisest person here on the farm. That is why I want to tell you my wishes regarding the disposition of my property and of my body. Because things will happen just as I say," she went on. "Even though you think there is nothing unusual about me, I assure you that evil will result if you disregard my wishes. Things have happened in such a way that I fear much harm will result in the end unless strong measures are taken."

Thórodd replied, "I do not doubt that you are pretty close to the truth in that. And for that reason I promise not to disregard your instructions."

Thorgunna said, "This is what I want you to do. If I die from this sickness, I want to have my body taken to Skálholt, for I have a feeling that that will sometime become the most celebrated place in this country.[4] I am sure also," she said, "that there are now priests there to sing a mass for me. For this reason I want you to have my body taken there. In return you are to have as much of my property as will reimburse you for your expense. Of my undivided possessions Thuríd is to have my scarlet cloak. I do this so that she will not take it amiss if I dispose of my other things as I wish. I want you to take as much of the property which I leave behind for my food and lodging as you or Thuríd want. I have a gold ring which I want to wear when I am taken to the

---

[3] This presageful omen is mentioned also elsewhere in the sagas as well as in the Icelandic Annals.

[4] Skálholt, in southwestern Iceland, became the site of the first Icelandic bishopric in 1056.

church. But my bedding and the bed furnishings are to be burned because they will bring no good to anyone, and I say this not because I begrudge anyone the enjoyment of these fine things. I would not do so if I knew they would be of use to someone. But I am so insistent about this because I would hate to have people suffer such great harm from me and my things as I know will come to them if they do not follow my instructions."

Thórodd promised to do as she had requested. After that Thorgunna's illness became worse. She was sick for only a few days before she died. The body was first taken to the church, and Thórodd had a coffin made for it. On the following day Thórodd had the bed furnishings brought outside and then fetched wood and made a large bonfire. Just then mistress Thuríd came up and asked Thórodd what he intended to do with the bedclothes. He said he was going to burn them all up as Thorgunna had stipulated.

"I don't want such splendid things burned," she said.

Thórodd replied, "She laid great stress on it that much harm would come of it if we did not follow her instructions."

Thuríd said, "That was nothing but envy. She begrudges other people the enjoyment of her things, and that's why she talked that way. No harm will come of it, whatever we do about this."

"I'm not sure," he said, "that things will not happen just as she predicted."

Then she put her arms around his neck and asked him not to burn the bed furnishings. She urged him so strongly that he finally changed his mind. The end of the matter was that Thórodd burned the feather beds and pillows and Thuríd got the quilts, the covers, and all the curtains and hangings. And yet neither one was completely satisfied with this outcome.

After this they made ready to transport the body; and reliable men and good horses, which belonged to Thórodd, were chosen to make this journey. The body was wrapped in linen cloth, but not sewed in it, and then placed in the coffin. They then set out, following the roadways which lead southward across the moors. Nothing unusual happened until they came south across the Valbjarnar Flats. Here they got into very soft quagmires, and the body often slipped off the horse. They proceeded southward to the Nordrá River and across the river at the Eyjarvad Ford. The river was very high. There were both strong gusts of wind and very heavy rain. They finally came to the farm called Lower

Ness on the Stafholts tongues of land.[5] They asked for food and lodging there, but the farmer refused to grant them hospitality.[6] Since it had grown late, they felt they could not continue any farther, for they thought the Hvítá River would be dangerous to cross at night. They unsaddled their horses and carried the body into a provision house near the house-door. They went into the sitting room and took off their clothes, assuming that they would have to spend the night there without food. The members of the household went to bed while it was still daylight. But when all had got into their beds, they heard a loud noise in the provision house. They went to see whether thieves might have broken in; and when they got there, they saw a large woman. She was completely naked, without a stitch of clothing on her, and she was busying herself at the cooking fire. Those who saw her were so frightened that they did not dare come near her. And when the men who had brought the body learned of this, they went there and saw how things stood. It was indeed Thorgunna, and it seemed advisable to all of them not to interfere with her. And when she had finished what she was doing, she carried the food into the room. Next she set the table and placed the food upon it.

Then the men who had brought the body said to the farmer, "It may well turn out, before we leave, that you will pay dearly for having refused us accommodations."

Then both the farmer and his wife said, "We will certainly give you food and grant you whatever other accommodations you need."

And as soon as the farmer had offered them hospitality, Thorgunna went out of the room and out of the house and did not appear again. Then a light was made in the room. The wet clothing was taken off the guests, and they were given dry things to put on. After that they sat down at the table and blessed the food, and the farmer had holy water sprinkled throughout the house. The guests ate their food, and no one suffered any harm even though Thorgunna had prepared it. They slept all that night, enjoying full hospitality.

In the morning they made ready to continue their journey, and they had no further difficulty. But wherever people heard of these events, most of them deemed it advisable to grant them whatever food and lodging they needed. The rest of the journey was uneventful. And

---

[5]The Stafholts tongues of land are formed by the junction of several swift rivers in a swampy plain.

[6]Refusal to grant food and lodging to people who were transporting a body for burial was later made a legal offense punishable by a fine of three marks.

when they came to Skálholt, the treasures which Thorgunna had intended for the church were delivered there, and the priests were glad
to receive them all. Thorgunna was buried there, and the men who had
brought her body returned home. They had a good journey and arrived
home safe and sound.

CHAPTER 52

The moon of weird.

At Fródá there was a large kitchen, at the rear of which was a locked
bed-closet, as was the custom at that time. In front, between the kitchen
and the outer door, were two storerooms, one on either side of the
passage. Dried fish was stored in one and flour in the other. Every
evening it was customary to make cooking fires in the kitchen. People
used to sit a long time by the fires before the evening meal was served.[1]
The evening the burial party returned, as the people were sitting at the
fires there, they saw a half moon appear on the wainscoting. It was
plain to see for all in the house. It went around the house from right to
left, withershins,[2] and it did not go away as long as the men sat by
the fire. Thórodd asked Thórir Woodenleg what that might portend.
Thórir replied that that was 'the moon of weird'—"and someone here
is fated to die." And this moon of ill fortune appeared every evening
that entire week.

---

[1] As soon as the light failed in the short winter days, people used to congregate
in the *eldskáli*—here translated 'kitchen' for lack of a more accurate term—by
the 'long fires' which were kept burning in the middle of the oblong 'hall'.

[2] I.e., in a direction contrary to the apparent course of the sun; which is of
sinister import.

CHAPTER 53

The spooks at Fródá.

IT HAPPENED NEXT that a shepherd came home greatly depressed. He spoke little, and what he did say was disagreeable. The people thought he must be bewitched, for he went about quite distracted and talking to himself. This went on for some time. When two weeks of winter had passed, the shepherd came home one evening, went to his bed, and lay down there. And next morning, when people came to his bed, he was dead. He was buried there at the church.

Very soon after that great hauntings began. One night Thórir Woodenleg went outside for a call of nature. And when he wanted to go back in, he saw the shepherd standing in front of the door. Thórir tried to enter, but the shepherd would not let him. Then Thórir tried to get away, but the shepherd ran after him, grabbed him, and threw him down against the door. He was badly hurt from this so that he was black and blue all over, but he managed to drag himself to his bed. He took sick from this and died. He was also buried at the church. Now both men, the shepherd and Thórir Woodenleg, haunted the place together. And because of this the people became greatly terrified, as was to be expected. After the death of Thórir a serving man of Thórodd took sick. He lay abed for three days before he died. Then one man after another died until six were dead.

By that time the Yule fast was approaching, though in those days the fasts were not observed in Iceland. The one storeroom was stacked so full of dried fish that the door could not be opened. The fish was piled all the way up to the crossbeam, and one had to use a ladder to get at the pile from the top. Now it happened several nights, while people were sitting by the kitchen fires, that they heard a noise in the storage room as though something were tearing the dried fish. But when they looked, they found nothing alive there.

One time that winter, shortly before Yule, farmer Thórodd went out to Ness for some of his dried fish. There were six of them in all, in a ten-oared boat, and they were gone all night. That same evening, after

Thórodd had left and when the kitchen fires were lit and people had come to sit by them, they saw a seal's head come up out of the fire pit. A serving woman, who was the first one to get there and to see this marvel, took up a cudgel which was lying in the doorway and struck the seal on the head with it. It only grew larger from the blow and glared up at the bed furnishings of Thorgunna.[1] Then a serving man went up and struck the seal, but it continued to come forth with every blow until the flippers could be seen. Then the serving man fell down in a faint. All who were there were struck with terror. Then the youth Kjartan ran up and seized a large sledge hammer and struck the seal on the head with it. It was a powerful blow, and the seal shook his head and looked around. Kjartan let blow after blow rain upon him, and the seal sank down like a peg being driven into the ground. He kept on striking until the seal had sunk down so far that he could pound the floor together over his head. And thus it always happened throughout the winter that all specters feared Kjartan most.

---

[1] Apparently the seal is the *fylgja* or attendant spirit of Thorgunna, who begrudges others the use of her belongings and wants to deprive them of their stored food.

CHAPTER 54

Thórodd drowns and haunts Fróдá.

ON THE NEXT MORNING, when Thórodd and his men rowed back from Ness with the dried fish, they all perished off the Enni Headland. The boat and the dried fish were washed up at the foot of Enni, but the bodies were not found. And when this news was learned at Fróдá, Kjartan and Thuríd invited their neighbors to celebrate the funeral feast there. The ale intended for the Yule feast was now taken and used for the funeral feast. But the first evening of the funeral feast, when the

guests had taken their seats, farmer Thórodd and his shipmates walked
into the hall, dripping wet. All welcomed Thórodd cordially since they
considered that a good omen. It was believed in those days that men who
had perished at sea and then came to attend their funeral feast had been
well received by Rán.[1] For at that time a great deal of heathendom still
prevailed even though all the people had been baptized and were nomi-
nally Christians. Thórodd and his men walked the length of the sitting
room and sleeping room, which had two doors, and out into the kitchen,
where they sat down at the fire without returning anyone's greeting.
The members of the household fled from the kitchen, but Thórodd and
his men remained sitting there until the fires had burned down to white
ashes. Then they vanished. This happened every evening as long as
the funeral feast lasted. There was much talk about this matter. Some
were of the opinion that the visits would stop when the funeral feast was
over.

When the people who had been invited to the feast returned home,
the house was rather lonely. The first evening after they had left, the
cooking fires were made as usual. And when the fires were burning,
Thórodd came in with his company, and they were dripping wet. They
sat down by the fires and began to wring out their clothing. And after
they had sat down, Thórir Woodenleg and his six followers came in.
They were all covered with earth. They shook out their clothing and
scattered the earth on Thórodd and his men. The people of the household fled from the kitchen, as was to be expected; and on that evening
they had neither light nor warmed stones[2] nor any other benefit from
the fire. On the following evening the cooking fire was made in another
room. It was thought that they would be less likely to come there. But
things did not turn out that way, for everything happened in the same
manner as on the previous evening. Both parties came to the fires.
On the third evening Kjartan suggested that they make one large fire in
the kitchen and the cooking fire in another room. This was done. The
result was that Thórodd and the others sat by the large fire, while
the members of the household sat by the small fire, and this continued
throughout the Yule season.

The disturbance in the pile of dried fish also increased more and more.
Day and night it sounded as though someone were tearing the stacked

---

[1]Rán, the goddess of the sea, was imagined as having a net in which she caught
drowning men to take them to her submarine abode—a sort of counterpart of Val-
halla.

[2]It is not clear whether these stones were used for warming food or the beds.

fish. There came the time when it was necessary to get some of the
dried fish. The man who climbed up saw a tail which looked like a
singed oxtail come up out of the pile. It was short and covered with
seal hair. The man who had climbed up to the top of the pile took hold
of the tail and pulled and asked the other people to come and help him.
They climbed up, both men and women, and pulled at the tail, but they
accomplished nothing. To all appearances the tail was that of a dead
animal. But while they were pulling the hardest, the tail suddenly
slipped through their hands and tore off the skin from the palms of those
who had taken the firmest grip. The tail was never seen again. Then
the dried fish was taken out, and it was seen that all the fish had been
torn from their skins so that only the skins remained. And when they
searched the pile to the bottom, they found not one living thing. Soon
after these events Thorgríma Galdrakin, the wife of Thórir Woodenleg,
took sick. She lay abed only a short while before she died; and on the
very evening of the day she was buried, she appeared in the train of
her husband Thórir. After the tail had appeared, the visitation was re-
newed; and now more women died than men. Six persons perished in a
row, and some fled from the hauntings and apparitions. In the autumn
there had been thirty servants in the household. Of these, eighteen had
died, five had fled, and only seven remained by the middle of February.

CHAPTER 55

Snorri helps banish the spooks.

BUT WHEN THESE MARVELS had reached this stage, Kjartan went to
Helgafell to see his uncle Snorri godi to ask his advice as to what was
to be done to deal with the visitations which had come upon them. By
that time the priest whom Gizur the White had sent to Snorri had arrived there. Snorri sent the priest to Fródá with Kjartan and his son

Thórd Cat and six additional men. He advised them to burn the bed furnishings of Thorgunna and to summon all the revenants to a court to be held at the door of the house. He asked the priest to conduct divine services there, to consecrate water, and to hear the people's confessions.[1] So they rode to Fródá and summoned men from the nearest farms to accompany them.

They arrived at Fródá on the evening before Candlemas[2] just as the kitchen fires were being lit. By that time mistress Thuríd had been taken ill in the same manner as those who had died. Kjartan went in at once and saw that Thórodd and his followers were sitting by the fire as was their custom. Kjartan took down the bed furnishings of Thorgunna. Then he went to the kitchen and fetched glowing embers from the fire; and going outside, he burned all the bed furnishings which had belonged to Thorgunna.

Thereupon Kjartan summoned Thórir Woodenleg, and Thórd Cat cited farmer Thórodd for haunting the house without permission and depriving people of health and life. All who were sitting by the fire were summoned. Then the door court was set up, the charges were stated, and the procedure was exactly as at an assembly court. The testimony of the witnesses was heard, the cases were summed up, and the verdicts given. When sentence was pronounced against Thórir Woodenleg, he got up and said, "Sat I have while the sitting was good."[3] Thereupon he left by way of the door before which the court was not being held.

Then sentence was pronounced against the shepherd. And when he heard it, he stood up and said, "Go I shall now, though I think I should have gone before."

And when Thorgríma Galdrakin heard sentence being pronounced over her, she arose and said, "Stayed I have while the staying was good."

Then each one in turn, as his sentence was pronounced, got up, said something, and left. It was obvious from these comments that they were all reluctant to leave.

---

[1] This chapter provides an excellent example of the interesting blending of earlier pagan and later Christian beliefs and attitudes which is characteristic of the saga as a whole.

[2] February 2. On this day candles were blessed and then borne in procession.

[3] All the sayings of the banished ghosts alliterate in the original, with just a hint of the comic.

Finally sentence was pronounced against farmer Thórodd. And when he heard it, he arose and said, "There's no welcome here; let's away all." Then he departed.

After that Kjartan and the others went in. The priest carried holy water and holy relics throughout the entire house. On the following day the priest conducted divine services and sang a solemn mass, after which all apparitions and hauntings at Fródá ceased. Thuríd recovered completely from her illness. In the spring following these marvels, Kjartan obtained servants and lived at Fródá for a long time afterward and became a most outstanding man.

CHAPTER 56

Snorri's feuds.

SNORRI GODI remained at Helgafell for eight years after the introduction of Christianity in Iceland. The last year he lived there was the one in which his father-in-law, Styr, was killed at Jorvi in Flisa parish. Snorri godi had gone south to that place for the body. At Hrossholt he had had to restrain Styr in the women's work room after Styr had sat up and seized the farmer's daughter about the waist.[1] In the following spring Snorri godi exchanged farms with Gudrún Ósvífrsdóttir, and Snorri moved all his property to Tongue in Sælingsdale. That was two years after the slaying of Gudrún's husband, Bolli Thorleiksson.[2]

In the autumn of the same year Snorri godi went south to Borgar Firth with four hundred men to initiate the prosecution for the killing

---

[1] In the *Heiðarvíga saga*, Chap. 9, this occurrence is told differently and with greater detail—how the farmer's daughter, consumed with curiosity to see the redoubtable Víga-Styr, at night approached the corpse and, when he seemed to sit up, fled in mad terror into Snorri's arms.

[2] Gudrún is the heroine of the *Laxdæla saga*.

of Styr. With him on this expedition were Styr's brother, Vermund the
Slender, who was then living in the Vatnsfjord, Steinthór of Eyr, Thórodd Thorbrandsson from Álptafirth, Thorleik Brandsson from Krossness, a nephew of Styr, and many other distinguished men. They came
as far south as Haugsvad Ford in the Hvítá River across from Bœr.
There, on the opposite side of the river, were Illugi the Black, Klepp-
járn the Old, Thorstein Gíslason, Gunnlaug Serpent-Tongue,[3] and
Thorstein Thorgilsson from Hafsfjord Island, who was married to
Vigdís, the daughter of Illugi the Black. There were many other distinguished men in their band, which numbered more than five hundred.
Thus Snorri and his men were prevented from riding south across the
river, and so they stated their case from the farthermost point they
could safely reach. Here Snorri cited Gest for the slaying of Styr. This
same case was rendered null and void for Snorri during the summer at
the Althing by Thorstein Gíslason. In the autumn of that year Snorri
godi rode south to Borgar Firth and killed Thorstein Gíslason and his
son Gunnar. With Snorri on that expedition were Steinthór of Eyr,
Thórodd Thorbrandsson, Bárd Hoskuldsson, and Thorleik Brandsson.
They were fifteen in all.

The following spring Snorri godi and Thorstein from Hafsfjord
Island, the son-in-law of Illugi the Black, met at the Thórsness Assembly. Thorstein was the son of Thorgils Thorfinnsson, who was the
son of Sel-Thórir from Raudamel. His mother was Aud, the daughter
of Álf from the Dales; and Thorstein was also a kinsman of Thorgils
Arason from Reykjahólar and of Thorgeir Hávarsson, Thorgils Holluson, Bitru-Oddi, and of the Álptafirth men Thorleif Kimbi and the
other sons of Thorbrand. Thorstein had prepared many cases for the
Thórsness Assembly. One day on the slope of the assembly grounds
Snorri asked Thorstein if he intended to present many cases at that
session. Thorstein replied that he had prepared several.

Snorri said, "Then I suppose you would like us to support your
cases the same way you Borgar Firth people supported our case last
spring?"

"No, I am not eager that you do," replied Thorstein.

And when Snorri godi had said that, his sons and many other kinsmen of Styr spoke up strongly and declared it would serve Thorstein
right if every one of his cases were blocked at the point they had then
reached. They said it would be fitting if Thorstein had to pay with his

---

[3]The skald Gunnlaug is the hero of the *Gunnlaugs saga*.

own head for the humiliation which he and his father-in-law Illugi had inflicted upon them the previous summer. Thorstein had little to say to this, and with that the men left the assembly hill.

Thorstein and his kinsmen, the people of Raudamel, had a large following there. And when it was time to go before the court, Thorstein made ready to present all the cases he had prepared. But when Styr's kinsmen and relatives by marriage learned of that, they armed themselves and took a position between the court and the men of Raudamel as they were trying to go to the court. A fight broke out between them. Thorstein of Hafsfjord Island was intent on only one thing, and that was to attack Snorri godi. Thorstein was not only big and strong, but also was a doughty fighter. And when Thorstein was pressing his attack on Snorri, Kjartan of Fródá, Snorri's nephew, ran in front of Snorri to protect him. Thorstein and Kjartan fought together for a long time and dealt each other severe blows. But then friends of both parties went between them and brought about a truce.

After the fight Snorri godi said to his nephew Kjartan, "Hard did you push the attack today, you Breidvíking!"

Kjartan replied quite angrily, "No need to reproach me for my paternity!"

In this battle seven of Thorstein's party were killed, and many were wounded on both sides. A reconciliation of the contending parties was brought about immediately at this assembly. Snorri did not quibble about the terms of arbitration since he did not want this case to come before the Althing. There was still the suit for the killing of Thorstein Gíslason pending against him, and he thought he had enough to answer for before the General Assembly without having this additional case to deal with. About all these events, the killing of Thorstein Gíslason and his son Gunnar and the battle at the Thórsness Assembly, Thormód Trefilsson composed this verse, which occurs in his poem *Hrafnsmál:*

34. Eke did the shield-shatterer
    shed two men's life-blood,
    slain in sword-contest
    south of the river.[4]
    Sithen lay there seven—
    seen are proofs thereof—
    thanes slain on Thórsness
    thingstead, and lifeless.

---

[4] I.e., the Hvítá River.

It was stipulated in the settlement that Thorstein should present all the lawsuits at the Thórsness Assembly which he had prepared. And at the General Assembly in the summer, an agreement was reached regarding the slaying of Thorstein Gíslason and his son Gunnar. And the men who had accompanied Snorri when he went to put these two to death made ready to go abroad.

That summer Thorstein of Hafsfjord Island transferred the godord authority of the Raudamel people from the Thórsness Assembly because he felt he had been overpowered by Snorri and his kinsmen.[5] He and his family established an assembly in the Straum Firth district and kept it up for a long time.

---

[5]Regarding the rights and duties of the godi and the godord office, cf. Chap. 4 and note 1 to Chap. 10.

CHAPTER 57

Óspak's robberies.

WHEN SNORRI GODI had been living at Tongue in Sælingsdale for several years, a man came to live to the north at Eyr by the Bitrafjord. His name was Óspak. He was the son of Kjallak from the Kjallaksá River by the promontory Skridinsenni. Óspak was married. He had a son named Glúm, who was still young at that time. Óspak was an extremely large and powerful man. He was much disliked and of a domineering disposition. He had seven or eight fellows with him who were always picking quarrels with the people there in the north. They always had a boat off the coast and helped themselves to whatever they pleased, both of other people's possessions and of things that drifted ashore on their beaches.[1] Álf the Little was the name of a man who lived in Thamb-

---

[1]Driftwood, whales, and other things washed ashore played an important part in the economy of the medieval Icelanders. Consequently, drift rights were jealously guarded. The whales, in particular, which provided many tons of meat, were greatly valued as a most prized addition to their rather monotonous diet.

árdale in the Bitra District. He was well-to-do and managed his farm
very well. He was a thingman of Snorri godi and supervised Snorri's
share of the shore drift by the Gudlaug Headland. Álf had occasion to
experience the hostility of Óspak and his band, and he always complained
of that to Snorri godi whenever they met.

Thórir Gull-Hardarson was then living at Tongue in the Bitrafjord
District. He was a friend of Sturla Thjódreksson, called Víga-Sturla,
who lived at Stadarhól in Saurbœ. Thórir was a highly esteemed farmer
and the leader in the Bitra District. He had the commission and custody
of the things drifted ashore belonging to Sturla up north there. Thórir
and Óspak were often at odds with each other; and now one, now the
other, got the upper hand. But Óspak was the leading man in Krossár-
dale and around the Enni Headland.

It happened one winter that severe weather set in early and put an
end to the grazing in the Bitra District. The people there suffered
great losses of livestock, and some of them drove their herds across the
mountains. The summer before, Óspak had had a fortification made on his
farm at Eyr. It was an excellent place for defense if there were reliable
men to man it. That winter, in February, there arose a violent storm
which lasted for a week. It was a strong gale from the north. And when
the storm abated, people saw that the drift ice had closed in all around,
but had not got in the Bitrafjord. Men then went out to search their
beaches. We are told that a large-sized Finback whale had been driven
ashore between Stika Ridge and the Gudlaug Headland. Snorri godi
and Sturla Thjódreksson had the greatest claim to the whale, but Álf
the Little and several other farmers were entitled to part of it. So men
flocked to the Bitrafjord to flense the whale and divide it according to the
directions of Thórir and Álf. And while they were busy cutting up the
whale, they saw a boat approaching from the other side of the fjord,
from the direction of Eyr. They recognized it as the big twelve-oared
boat which belonged to Óspak. He and his men landed near the whale
and went ashore—fifteen men in all and heavily armed. When Óspak
came ashore, he walked up to the whale and asked who had charge of
it. Thórir replied that he was responsible for the part which belonged
to Sturla, while Álf was supposed to look out for his own portion and
that of Snorri godi. "And after that each of the other farmers is entitled to his share." Óspak asked how much of the whale they would
give him.

Thórir replied, "I will not give you any of the portion I am responsible for, and I do not know if the farmers wish to sell any of their share. For that matter, how much are you willing to pay?"

"You know, Thórir," said Óspak, "that I am not in the habit of buying whale meat from you people around the Bitrafjord."

"And yet," retorted Thórir, "it seems more than likely to me that you will not get any unless you buy it."

The pieces which had been cut from the whale were lying in a pile and had not been apportioned yet. Óspak ordered his men to go and carry this meat to the ship. Those who were working on the whale had few weapons except the axes with which they were cutting the whale. But when Thórir saw that Óspak and his men were approaching the whale, he called to his men that they should not let themselves be robbed. Then they ran to the other side of the whale, and the men who were still busy flensing also came running, Thórir at their head. Óspak immediately turned on him and struck him with the blunt part of his axe. The blow caught him on the temple, and he fell down unconscious. Those who were closest to him took hold of him, pulled him back, and crowded around him while he lay unconscious. But then no one was guarding the whale. Then Álf the Little came up and asked Óspak's men not to take any of the whale.

Óspak said, "You keep out of this, Álf. You have a thin skull, and I have a heavy axe. You will fare worse than Thórir if you come one step closer."

Álf thought it wise to heed this warning. Óspak and his men carried the cut meat down to the boat and had finished doing that by the time Thórir regained consciousness. And when he realized what had happened, he upbraided his men and said they had behaved shamefully, just standing idly by while some men were being robbed and others beaten. Then Thórir sprang up. But Óspak and his band had already got the ship afloat and had shoved off. They rowed westward over the fjord to Eyr and were busy there with their catch. Óspak did not permit any of the men who had taken part in the raid to leave. They made their quarters in the fortress and remained there. Thórir and the others divided up what was left of the whale, and all shared the loss in proportion to the sizes of their allotments. When this was completed, they all returned home. Thereafter Thórir and Óspak were at open war with one another. But because there was such a large number of men with Óspak, the whale meat they had stolen was soon consumed.

CHAPTER 58

Thórir pursues Óspak.

ONE NIGHT Óspak and fourteen men went to Thambárdale and broke into Álf's house. They drove Álf and his entire household into the sitting room while they plundered at will there. They loaded their booty on four pack-horses. But people had caught sight of them from Fjardarhorn farm and had sent a man to Tongue to tell Thórir. Thórir at once gathered men and they rode, eighteen strong, down to the head of the fjord. Thórir saw Óspak and his band ahead of him, proceeding north-ward from Fjardarhorn farm.

When Óspak became aware that he was being followed, he said, "I see men coming there, most likely Thórir; he probably intends to avenge himself for the blow I gave him this winter. There are eighteen of them and fifteen of us, but we are better equipped. It remains to be seen which of us will crow over the victory this time. But the horses we took from Thambárdale will probably run home [if we leave them unguarded], and I do not want to lose what we have once laid our hands on. So two of you men who are not so heavily armed drive the pack-horses ahead of us to Eyr and send the men who are at home out here to help us. We thirteen will face them here as well as we can."

They did as Óspak told them. And when Thórir and his men caught up with him, Óspak greeted them and asked the news. He spoke pleas-antly, intending thus to delay Thórir's attack. Thórir asked where they had got their provisions. Óspak replied that they had got them at Thambárdale.

"How did you get them?" asked Thórir.

"They were neither given as gifts nor ceded by sale,"[1] replied Óspak.

"Will you give them up then," asked Thórir, "and turn them over to us?"

Óspak said he did not feel inclined to do that. Then they rushed at each other and the fight began. Thórir and his men attacked most fiercely, but Óspak and his companions defended themselves doughtily.

---

[1] An alliterative phrase in the original.

They were too strongly outnumbered, however, and some of them were wounded and others were killed. Thórir was armed with a bear spear, and he ran at Óspak, thrusting at him; but Óspak parried the blow, and since Thórir had lunged with all his strength without striking anything with his spear, he fell forward on his hands and knees. Óspak then struck Thórir on the back with his axe so that there was a resounding clang.

Óspak said, "That will discourage you from taking long journeys, Thórir."

Thórir retorted, "Maybe, but many a day's journey I mean to make in spite of you and your blow."

Thórir had been wearing a knife on a strap around his neck, as was the custom then, and had slung it behind him, and Óspak's blow had struck that; and so he had received only two light wounds on both sides of the back. Thereupon one of Thórir's men ran up and aimed a blow at Óspak, but he parried it with his axe. The blow cut the shaft in two so that the blade fell down. Then Óspak called to his men and told them to beat a retreat. He himself took to his heels. But Thórir jumped up and immediately hurled his spear after Óspak. It struck him in the thigh and came out on the other side. Óspak jerked the spear from the wound and whirled around. He sent it flying back and it struck in the middle the man who had slashed at Óspak before, and he fell down dead. After that Óspak and his gang fled, and Thórir and his men pursued them along the shore almost as far as Eyr. Then people came running from the farm, both men and women, and Thórir and his men turned back. There were no more attacks that winter. In this skirmish three of Óspak's men and one of Thórir's were killed, and many were wounded on both sides.

CHAPTER 59

Óspak continues his robberies.

SNORRI GODI took charge of all accusations against Óspak and his gang by Álf the Little, and he had all of them outlawed at the Thórsness Assembly. After the assembly Snorri godi rode home to Tongue and remained there until the day of the court of execution.[1] Then he rode north to the Bitrafjord with a numerous following. But when he got there, Óspak and all his people were gone. They had taken two boats and, fifteen strong, had sailed north to the Strands.[2] They remained there during the summer and committed many outrages. They settled down by the Tharalátrs Fjord and gathered men about them; among others a fellow whose name was Hrafn, but who was called the Viking, joined them. He was a desperado who had his haunts by the North Strands as an outlaw. There they ravished the countryside, killing and plundering, until winter set in. Then Óláf Eyvindarson from Drangar and some other farmers banded together and attacked them. There, too, in the Tharalátrs Fjord they had a fortification around their dwelling and were in all almost thirty men. Óláf and his men laid siege to the fortification, but they thought it would be difficult to overcome. And so they parleyed with them, and the evildoers agreed to leave the Strands and commit no more outrages there. Also they were to abandon their fortification there. And since the farmers felt that they were not in a favorable position to fight it out, they accepted those conditions, and both parties pledged themselves to abide by them. Thereupon the farmers went home.

---

[1]The court of execution (or forfeiture) was held fourteen days after the sentence had been passed, usually on the farm of the convicted man.

[2]The deeply indented, mountainous east coast of the northwestern peninsula of Iceland.

CHAPTER 60

Thórir is killed by Óspak. Álf flees.

SNORRI GODI, as was written above, had gone north to Bitra to hold the court of execution; and when he came there, Óspak was already gone. Snorri held the court of execution according to law. He confiscated all the property of the outlaws and divided it among the men against whom they had committed the greatest outrages, Álf the Little and the other men who had previously been robbed. Then Snorri godi rode home to Tongue, and thus the summer passed.

Óspak and his band left the Strands at the beginning of winter with their two large boats. They rowed south along the Strands and then north across the Húnaflói Fjord[1] to the Vatnsness Peninsula. There they went ashore and pillaged, loading their boats with as much booty as they could hold. Then they re-crossed the Húnaflói Fjord to the Bitra-fjord and landed at Eyr and carried their booty up into the fortification. Óspak's wife and their son Glúm had remained there during the summer with two cows.

The same night they returned home, the robbers rowed in to the head of the fjord in both boats. They went up to the farm at Tongue and broke open the house there. They pulled farmer Thórir from his bed, led him outside, and killed him. Then they looted the house and took everything they found there and put it in their boats. Then they rowed to Thambárdale, ran up to the house, and broke down the door as they had at Tongue. Álf the Little had been sleeping fully dressed. When he heard the door being broken down, he sprang up and escaped through a secret door at the back of the house[2] and ran up the valley. Óspak and his men robbed him of everything they could lay their hands on and took it to their boats. They rowed home to Eyr with both boats loaded and carried this booty up into the fortification. They also dragged

---

[1] Actually, east.

[2] Secret doors are mentioned frequently in the sagas. Sometimes underground passages extended a considerable distance from the house to a concealed exit.

the boats up into the fortification, filled them with water, and then barred the gates—it was an excellent stronghold—and remained there for the winter.

CHAPTER 61

Snorri summons Thránd.

ÁLF THE LITTLE ran south across the mountains and did not stop until he came to Tongue, and he told Snorri godi about his troubles. He strongly urged that they should go north immediately to attack Óspak and his men. But Snorri godi first wanted to know what else they had done there in the north besides routing him and also whether they had settled down by the Bitrafjord. Somewhat later the news came from the north of the slaying of Thórir and of the preparations Óspak had made. Also it was learned that it would probably not be an easy matter to attack them.

Thereupon Snorri godi had Álf's entire household and all his remaining possessions brought to Tongue, and they stayed there for the winter. Enemies of Snorri godi reproached him for being so slow in doing something for Álf. Snorri let them say what they pleased about that, neither was anything done. Sturla Thjódreksson sent word from the west that he was ready to proceed against Óspak whenever Snorri wished him to and declared that he was no less obligated to do so than Snorri. The winter wore on and Yule passed, and there were constant reports from the north about the ravages perpetrated by Óspak and his gang. Very severe weather prevailed, and all the fjords were frozen over. Shortly before Lent, Snorri godi sent a messenger to Ingjaldshvál on Snæfellsness.[1] A man lived there who was called Thránd the Strider. He was

---

[1] The farm of *Ingjaldshváll* ('Ingjald's Knoll') is located near the extreme tip of the Snæfellsness peninsula. The distance from there to Snorri's residence at Sælingsdale as the crow flies is some 50 miles. Covering it on foot in a day over rough and wintry terrain is a superhuman feat.

the son of that Ingjald for whom the farm Ingjaldshvál is named. Thránd was extremely large and strong and exceedingly swift of foot. He had been a follower of Snorri before, and he was thought to be a werewolf while he was still a pagan, but most men lost their troll nature when they were baptized.[2] Snorri sent a message that Thránd should meet him at Tongue and be prepared to face danger.

When Thránd received Snorri's message, he said, "You rest here as long as you like. I shall go as Snorri bids me, but you will not be able to keep up with me."

The messenger replied that he would believe that when he saw it. But in the morning when the messenger awoke, Thránd was already gone. He had taken his weapons and passed under the headland of Enni. Then he took the roadway to the Búland Headland and, skirting the fjords, made his way to the farm called Eid. From there he crossed the Kolgrafafjord and the Seljafjord on the ice. Then he traveled to the Vigrafjord and along the ice till he reached the head of the fjord. He arrived at Tongue in the evening just as Snorri was sitting at table. Snorri gave him a friendly welcome. Thránd returned the greeting and asked what Snorri wanted of him. He said he was ready to undertake any journey on which Snorri wished to send him. Snorri told him to stay there and rest for the night. Then Thránd was helped out of his wet clothes.

---

[2] The term in the original *(hann var eigi einhamr)* refers to the belief that a wizard could 'shift shape'—generally into that of a large animal, such as a bear or a wolf, with its strength or swiftness. That Thránd in the first decennium after the introduction of Christianity had become firm in the faith is a bit unlikely!

CHAPTER 62

Óspak's fort is attacked. His band is dispersed.

THAT SAME NIGHT Snorri sent a man west to Stadarhól and asked Sturla Thjódreksson to join him at Tongue at the head of the Bitrafjord on the following day. Snorri also sent messengers to the nearest farms to summon men. The day after, they set out from Tongue northward across Gaflfell Heath with fifty men. They arrived at Tongue in Bitra in the evening. Sturla was already there with thirty men. They continued on to Eyr during the night. And when they arrived there, Óspak came out on the wall of their fortification with some of his followers and asked who headed this body of men. They told him and then asked him to surrender, but Óspak declared he would not.

"But we will give you the same choice as we gave the people at the Strands," he said. "If you do not attack us, we will move out of the district."

Snorri stated that he would not let them prescribe any such conditions for him.

On the following morning, as soon as it was light, they divided their forces to attack the fortification from different sides. Snorri was to attack where Hrafn the Viking had charge of the defense, while Sturla was to attack where Óspak manned the defense. Sám and Thormód, the sons of Bork the Stout, attacked on one side, while Snorri's sons, Thórodd and Thorstein Thorskabít, struck at another. Óspak and his men used stones for defense, all they could lay hold of. They used them unsparingly as the men inside the fort were hard fighters. For the attack Snorri and Sturla used chiefly arrows and javelins. They had a good supply of these since they had been preparing for a long time to take the stronghold. The attack was extremely fierce. Many were wounded on both sides, but no one was killed. Snorri and his men kept up such a hail of missiles that Hrafn and his followers had to withdraw behind the walls. At that point Thránd the Strider took a run at the wall and leaped up so high that he was able to hook his axe over the top of it. Then he pulled himself up hand over hand along the haft until he gained the top of the wall. But when Hrafn saw that a man had got into the fort, he rushed at Thránd and thrust at him with his spear; but Thránd parried the thrust, hewed at Hrafn, and cut off his arm at the shoulder. After that so many came at him that he let himself drop down from the wall and so got back to his own side.

Óspak urged on his men to defend themselves, and he himself fought most daringly, going far out on the walls of the stronghold to hurl stones. One time, when he put forth all his strength to throw a rock into the midst of Sturla's men, Sturla hurled a javelin with a thong at him. It struck him in the middle, and he fell down outside the fort. Sturla ran up at once to set on him and would not permit anyone else to attack him because he wanted it to be known for sure that it was he who slew Óspak.

A third man fell from the wall which the sons of Bork were attacking. After that the robbers offered to surrender if the attackers would guarantee them safety of life and limb. They offered also to place it entirely in the hands of Snorri godi and Sturla what was to be done with them. And since Snorri and his men had almost exhausted their arrows and javelins, they agreed to this. The stronghold was surrendered and its defenders gave themselves up to Snorri, who guaranteed them safety of life and limb as they had stipulated. Both Óspak and Hrafn died, as well as a third man of their band, while many on both sides were wounded. Thus said Thormód in the *Hrafnsmál*:

> 35. Battle was in Bitra;
>   bounteous food gave there
>   the brisk battle-lord to
>   birds-of-valkyries.[1]
>   Of life reft lay there
>   leaders-of-seasteeds,[2]
>   vikings three, by victor
>   vanquished. He ravens battened.

Snorri permitted Óspak's wife and their son Glúm to remain living there. Glúm later married Thórdís, the daughter of Ásmund Hoary Head and the sister of Grettir the Strong. Their son was that Óspak who contended with Odd Ófeigsson in Midfjord. Snorri and Sturla sent each of the robbers on his way and so scattered this band of evildoers. Then they

---

[1]Kenning for 'raven'.
[2]Kenning for 'warriors'.

went home. Thránd the Strider remained at Snorri's place for a short while before continuing home to Ingjaldshvál, and Snorri thanked him well for his help. Thránd the Strider dwelled for a long time at Ingjaldshvál, and after that at Thrándarstead, and he was a man to reckon with.

CHAPTER 63

Thórólf haunts the Álptafirth District again. His body is burned.
—Thórodd is killed by the bull Glæsir.

AT THAT TIME Thórodd Thorbrandsson was living in the Álptafirth District. He owned the two farms, Úlfarsfell and Orlygsstead, but by that time the visitations of Thórólf Lamefoot were so alarming that people felt they could not live there any longer. Bólstead was left deserted because Thórólf had begun to haunt the place again as soon as Arnkel was dead, and he had killed both men and livestock there, so that no one dared to live there. And after Bólstead had become altogether desolate, Lamefoot moved up to Úlfarsfell and caused great trouble there. All the people became filled with dread as soon as they became aware of his presence there. Then the farmer at Úlfarsfell went to Kársstead to complain to Thórodd about his trouble, because he was Thórodd's tenant. He declared that people thought that Lamefoot would not stop until the entire fjord district was deserted by both humans and livestock unless steps were taken against him—"and I shall not be able to hold out there longer if nothing is done." And when Thórodd heard that, he thought it might be difficult to do much about it.

On the following morning Thórodd had his horses brought. He summoned both his men servants as well as people from the neighboring farms to go along. They rode on to Bægifót Headland and the mound of Thórólf. They broke open his burial mound and found Thórólf in it. His body was still undecayed and most troll-like in appearance. He was as black as Hel[1] and as big around as an ox. And when they tried to get him out, they were unable to budge him. Then Thórodd had them shove a piece of wood underneath him, and by that means they pried him up out of his grave. Then they trundled him down to the beach. Here they piled up a large heap of wood, rolled Thórólf onto it, and set it on fire. They let the wood and Thórólf burn to cold ashes. Yet it was a long time before the fire took hold of Thórólf. There was a strong wind blowing, and the ashes were scattered far and wide after the fire had begun to burn. But they raked as much of the ashes as they could out into the water. And after finishing this task, they rode home.

Thórodd himself returned to Kárssteadt late in the evening, and the women were then busy milking. When he rode up to the milking shed, a cow shied away from him, fell, and broke her leg. They took hold of her, but she was too lean to make it worth while to slaughter her. Then Thórodd had the leg bandaged, but the cow went dry. When the leg was healed, she was led up to Úlfarsfell for fattening, for there the pasture was as good as on an island.[2] The cow often came down to the shore where the funeral pile had been and licked the stones on which the ashes had lain. It was said that one time when men from the islands came rowing up to the head of the fjord with a boatload of dried fish, they saw the cow up on the hillside together with a dapple-gray bull.[3] No one knew there was such a bull in the neighborhood.

In the autumn Thórodd intended to slaughter the cow; but when men went out to look for her, she was nowhere to be found. Thórodd often had her searched for that fall, but she was never found. People assumed she had died or else had been stolen. Early one morning shortly before Yule the herdsman at Kárssteadt went to the cowshed as usual. There he saw the cow standing before the gate of the shed, and he recognized the animal as being the same which had broken its leg and then had been lost. He led her into a stall, tied her, and went to tell Thórodd. He went to the shed, looked at the cow, and felt her with his hands. They found that she was with calf and so was unfit for slaughter. Also, Thórodd had

---

[1]Hel, the goddess of the nether world, is pictured as being half black and half flesh-colored.

[2]The islands of the north have excellent grass both because they are fertilized by bird droppings and also because they are usually not overgrazed.

[3]The color indicates his supernatural origin. In the legendary tales of the north, animals of this color are thought of as coming out of, and returning to, some body of water or the sea. In this case, Glæsir, sired by this bull with the cow that had licked the ashes of Thórólf, takes vengeance on Arnkel's successor, then returns to his element.

slaughtered as much as he needed for his household anyway. In the following spring, just before the beginning of summer, the cow had a calf. It was a heifer. And after a little while she had another calf. That was a bull calf. She had great difficulty bringing it forth because it was so large. A little later the cow died.

This large calf was carried into the sitting room. It was dapple-gray in color, and well worth having. Now both calves were in the room, the first-born one having already been brought in. An old woman was sitting in the room. She was Thórodd's foster mother and had become blind. In her younger days she had been considered second-sighted; but now that she had grown old, what she said was regarded as senile chatter. Yet many things happened as she had foretold. When the large calf was trussed up on the floor, it bawled out loudly.

When the old woman heard that, she became greatly frightened and said, "That is the voice of a troll, and not of any other living creature. Do, please, slaughter this evil-boding monster."

Thórodd said there was no reason to kill the calf. He said it was excellently fit to be raised and would make a fine animal when fully grown. Right then the calf bellowed a second time. Then the old woman trembled all over and said, "Dear foster son, do have this calf slaughtered, for misfortune will come to us if you raise it."

He replied, "The calf shall be slaughtered if you so wish, foster mother."

Then both calves were carried out. Thórodd had the heifer calf slaughtered and the other one taken out to the barn. He issued a warning that no one should tell the old woman that the bull calf was alive.

This calf grew visibly day by day, so that in the spring when the calves were let out of the stable, it was no smaller than those which had been born at the beginning of the winter. He rampaged about the homefield when he got out, bellowing as loudly as a full-grown bull, so that he was clearly heard in the house.

Then the old woman said, "So that troll was not killed after all. Now more harm will come to us from it than words can tell."

The calf grew rapidly and was pastured in the homefield during the summer. By autumn he was so large that few yearling steers were larger. He had a good set of horns and was very handsome in appearance. He was called Glæsir. When he was two years old, he was as large as a five-year-old ox; he was always kept on the farm with the milking cows. And whenever Thórodd came to the milking pen, Glæsir went up to him and sniffed at him and licked his clothing, and Thórodd patted him.

He was as gentle as a sheep among both men and animals. But when he bellowed, it sounded most frightening; and whenever the old woman heard that, she became terribly excited.

When Glæsir was four years old, he refused to go out of the way for women, children, or young men. And if grown men went at him, he tossed his head and acted enraged; still he retreated before them if he had to. One day when Glæsir came home to the milking shed, he bellowed so loudly that it could be heard as clearly indoors as nearby. Thórodd and the old woman were in the sitting room.

She sighed heavily and said, "You don't value my advice very highly, not having that bull killed, foster son."

Thórodd replied, "Never mind, foster mother. We are going to let Glæsir live until fall and then slaughter him after he has put on some flesh during the summer."

"Very likely it will be too late then," she said.

"That remains to be seen," said Thórodd.

While they were saying this, the bull bellowed, and it sounded more horrible than before. Then the old woman spoke this verse:

36. His head beats the herd's leader,
     hoary chieftain, bellowing—
     that bull, fear I, will be men's
     bane—with voice blood-curdling;
     to the grave will he teach you
     travel, I forewarn you:
     that ox eftsoons your life will
     end: I still see clearly.

Thórodd replied, "That is nothing but doting old wives' babble. I don't believe you see that."

She spoke this verse:

37. Always when the old one
     opes her mouth—"she is doting"—
     but I see gore from bloody
     belly dripping—say you.
     Madly turning on mankind—
     mark you my words—that brute will—
     that sees the Gerd-of-glittering-
     goldrings[4]—be your death yet.

---

[4]Gerd is a goddess; the whole, a (rather inappropriate) kenning for 'woman'.

"That will not happen, foster mother," he declared.

"Alas, but it will," she said.

During the summer, after Thórodd had had all the hay in the home-field raked into large haycocks, there came a heavy rain. In the morning when the men came out of the house, they saw that Glæsir had got into the homefield. He had got the piece of wood off his horns which had been fastened there when he had begun to be mean. Formerly he had never harmed the hay when he was in the homefield, but now he had lost his former habits. He ran at the haycocks, stuck his horns underneath, lifted them up, and scattered them over the field. As soon as one was ruined, he attacked another. Thus he ran about in the field, bellowing and acting as if he were mad. The men were in such great dread of him that all were afraid to go and chase him out of the field.

When they told Thórodd what Glæsir was doing, he ran out at once. From a pile of wood which stood by the door, he snatched a big birchwood cudgel and swung it about his head, holding it by its branches, and ran down onto the field toward the bull. When Glæsir saw him, he stopped and turned toward him. Thórodd berated him, but the bull did not yield ground for all that. Then Thórodd raised the cudgel and struck him so hard between the horns that it broke at the point where the branches grew out. The blow enraged Glæsir so that he charged. Thórodd succeeded in seizing the horns and turning him aside, and thus it went for a while, Glæsir charging and Thórodd eluding him and turning him alternately from one side to the other, until Thórodd began to tire. Then he sprang up on the bull's withers and put his arms around his neck, putting his weight forward on the bull's head, trying to wear him out. But the bull ran back and forth across the field with him. Then the members of Thórodd's household saw that he was in a precarious position, but they did not dare go to his help without weapons. They went in for their weapons; and when they came out, they ran down to the homefield with spears and other weapons. When the bull saw that, he thrust his head down between his front legs and twisted it so that he was able to get one horn under Thórodd. Then he tossed his head so quickly that Thórodd's legs were thrown up in the air and he almost stood on his head on the bull's neck. And when Thórodd slid down, Glæsir got his head under him and thrust one horn deep into his abdomen. Then Thórodd let go his hold; and uttering a wild bellow, the bull ran across the field down to the river. Thórodd's men ran after Glæsir and chased him across the landslide Geirvor and all the way to a quagmire below the farm Hellur. There the bull ran out into the quagmire and sank down and never came up again. That quagmire is now called Glæsiskelda ('Glæsir's Bog').

When Thórodd's men returned to the homefield, they found he had gone back to the farm. And when they entered the house, they saw Thórodd lying on his bed dead. He was taken to the church. Thórodd's son Kár took over the farm in Álptafirth after his father's death and lived there for a long time. The farm was named Kársstead for him.

CHAPTER 64

Gudleif finds Bjorn in an unknown land.

THERE WAS A MAN named Gudleif, who was the son of Gunnlaug the Wealthy of Straum Firth and the brother of Thorfinn, from whom the Sturlungs are descended. Gudleif was a great merchant. He owned a large trading vessel; and Thórólf, the son of Eyra-Lopt, owned another one the time they fought with Gyrd, the son of Earl Sigvaldi.[1] In this battle Gyrd lost an eye.

In the latter days of King Óláf the Saint,[2] Gudleif made a merchant voyage westward to Dublin. And when he left there, he intended to return to Iceland. Sailing west of Ireland, he got counterwinds from the east and northeast and was driven far west and southwest out of his course so that they did not know where they were. By then the summer drew to a close, and they made many vows that they might reach land; and at last they caught sight of land. It was a large land, but no one knew which country it was. Gudleif and his men decided to approach it because they thought it unwise to stay longer on the high seas. They

---

[1]Sigvaldi, a powerful Danish earl, became the leader of the Jómsvíkings after Palnatóki's death.
[2]He died A.D. 1030.

found a good harbor there, but they had made land only a short while when some men came up to them. They knew no one there, but they rather thought that those people spoke Irish. Soon such a large crowd gathered that there must have been many hundreds. They attacked Gudleif's men, made them all captive, and tied their hands; and then they drove them inland. They were taken to some meeting where sentence was to be passed on them. They gathered that some wanted them killed while others were for having them apportioned to various places and made slaves.

While this was being debated, they saw a band of men under a banner approaching on horseback, and they supposed that there must be some chieftain among them. And when this band drew nearer, they saw a tall man of martial bearing riding under the banner. He was quite advanced in years and his hair was white. All those who were there bowed before him and greeted him as their lord. They soon discovered that all measures and decisions were referred to him. Then this man had Gudleif and his men brought up to him; and when they came before him, he spoke to them in Norse and asked what country they were from. They told him that most of them were Icelanders. He asked which of them were Icelanders. Thereupon Gudleif stepped up and greeted him, and he returned the greeting and asked what part of Iceland they were from. Gudleif said they were from the Borgar Firth district. Then he asked what part of Borgar Firth they were from, and Gudleif told him. Thereupon he asked very carefully about every single one of the more important personages in the Borgar Firth and Broad Firth districts. And in the course of their conversation he asked about Snorri godi and his sister Thuríd of Fródá; and he asked particularly about all matters at Fródá and most of all about the youth Kjartan, who by then was the farmer at Fródá.

The countrymen called out again, demanding that some decision be made about the ship's crew. Then this tall man stepped aside and told off twelve of his men to advise him, and they sat deliberating for a long time. Thereupon they returned to the place where the crowd was gathered.

The tall man addressed Gudleif and his men as follows: "We people of this country have discussed your case, and the others have agreed to place your fate in my hands. I will grant you permission to sail where-ever you want to. Even though you may think it is rather late in the summer for that, I advise you to leave this place because these people are not to be trusted and are hard to deal with. They consider that their laws have been broken [in your coming here and leaving with your lives].

Gudleif asked, "Who shall we say procured us our freedom if fate grants us a return to our native country?"

He replied, "That I shall not tell you, for I do not wish my kinsmen and foster brothers the sort of reception here which you would have had if it had not been for me. But now I have grown so old that it is not unlikely that death may carry me off any moment. And even though I live for a while longer, there are men in this country more powerful than I am who will make short shrift of foreigners even though they may not come so close to us as you have."

Then this man had their ship made ready for them, and he remained there with them until a favorable wind came and they could put out from shore. But before he and Gudleif parted, he took a gold ring from his arm and placed it and also a good sword in Gudleif's hands.

He said to Gudleif, "If fate permits you to reach the land of your birth, take this sword to Kjartan, the farmer at Fródá, and this ring to Thuríd, his mother."

Gudleif asked, "Who shall I say sent these precious things?"

He replied, "Say that he sent them who was a better friend to the mistress of the house at Fródá than to her brother, the godi at Helgafell. But if anyone thinks he knows from this who was the owner of these things, then tell them this: that I forbid any and every man to try to find me because that is an extremely hazardous undertaking unless they have the same good luck in landing as you did. For this is a large country, with few harbors, and people everywhere are hostile to foreigners unless they are as fortunate as you."

With that they parted.

Gudleif and his companions put out to sea and landed in Ireland late in the fall. They spent the winter in Dublin. In the summer following they sailed to Iceland, and Gudleif delivered the gifts. And all were certain that this man was Bjorn the Breidavík Champion; but there is no other information available concerning that than what has been told here.

CHAPTER 65

Snorri's descendants and his death.

SNORRI GODI lived at Tongue for twenty years. At first his residence there was rather resented as long as those two overbearing men, Thorstein Kuggason and Thorgils Holluson, and other chieftains who were his enemies were alive. He occurs in many other sagas. Thus he occurs in *Laxdæla saga,* as is known to many. He was a great friend of Gudrún Ósvífrsdóttir and her sons. He occurs also in *Heidarvíga saga,* where next to Gudmund the Mighty he was the strongest supporter of Bardi after the Heidarvíg battle. But as Snorri began to age, his popularity increased. This was partly because the number of those who envied him had dwindled. The number of his friends was increased also by the fact that he had established connections through marriage far and wide with the greatest men in the Broad Firth District and elsewhere. He married his daughter Sigríd to Brand the Swift, the son of Vermund. Later she was married to Kolli, the son of Thormód, the son of Thorlák of Eyr; they lived in Bjarnarhaven. He gave his daughter Unn in marriage to Víga-Bardi. Later she was married to Sigurd, the son of Thórir the Dog,[1] on the island Bjarkey in the Hálogaland District. Their daughter was Rannveig, who was married to Jón, the son of Árni, the son of Árni Ármódsson; and their son was Vidkunn of Bjarkey, who became one of the greatest of the king's stewards in Norway. Snorri godi married his daughter Thórdís to Bolli Bollason, and from them are descended the Gilsbekkings. Snorri's daughter Hallbera was married to Thórd, the son of Sturla Thjódreksson. Their daughter was Thuríd, who was married to Haflidi, the son of Már; and a great family claims descent from them. His daughter Thóra, Snorri married to Keru-Bersi, the son of Halldór Óláfsson from Hjardarholt. Later she was married to Thorgrím Svidi, and from them have come a large and respected family. The other daughters of Snorri godi were married after his death: Thuríd the Wise to Gunnlaug, the son of Steinthór of Eyr; Gudrún

---

[1] A chieftain of Hálogaland (Helgeland) and one of the antagonists of Saint Óláf of Norway.

to Kálf of Sólheimar; Halldóra to Thorgeir from Ásgardshólar; and Álof to Jorund Thorfinnsson, the brother of Gunnlaug from Straum Firth.

Halldór was the most highly regarded of the sons of Snorri godi. He lived in Hjardarholt in Laxárdale. From him are descended the clan of the Sturlungs and the people of Vatnsfjord. Next to him, Thórodd was the most highly regarded son of Snorri. He lived at Spákonufell in Skaga Strand. Snorri's son Máni lived at Saudafell. His son was Ljót, who was called Mána-Ljót. He was regarded as the most eminent of Snorri's grandsons. Snorri's son Thorstein lived at Laugarbrekka, and from him are descended the Ásbirnings in Skagafjord and a large family. Of Snorri's other sons, Thórd Cat lived in Dufgusdale, Eyjólf lived at Lambastead at Mýrar, and Thorleif lived at Medalfell Strands. From him are descended the Ballæring people. Snorri Snorrason lived at Tongue in Sælingsdale after the death of his father. Klepp was the name of one of Snorri's sons, but it is not known where he lived or who his descendants were, as far as reports go.

Snorri godi died at Tongue in Sælingsdale the year after the fall of King Óláf the Saint. He was buried there at the church which he himself had had built. But when the churchyard was dug up, his bones were taken up and brought down to the church which is there now. Gudný Bodvarsdóttir, the mother of the Sturlusons Snorri, Thórd, and Sighvat,[2] was present on that occasion; and she stated that they were the bones of an average-sized man and not large. She said that they also exhumed the bones of Bork the Stout, the paternal uncle of Snorri godi; and she said that these were exceedingly large. She said that the bones of good-wife Thórdís, the daughter of Thorbjorn Súr and the mother of Snorri godi, were also taken up then; and Gudný said that they were the bones of a little woman and as black as though they had been burned. All these bones were interred where the church now stands. And here ends the saga of the people of Thórsness, Eyr, and Álptafirth.

---

[2] These great chieftains lived in the first part of the 13th century.

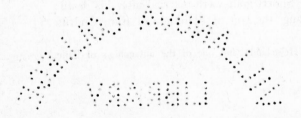

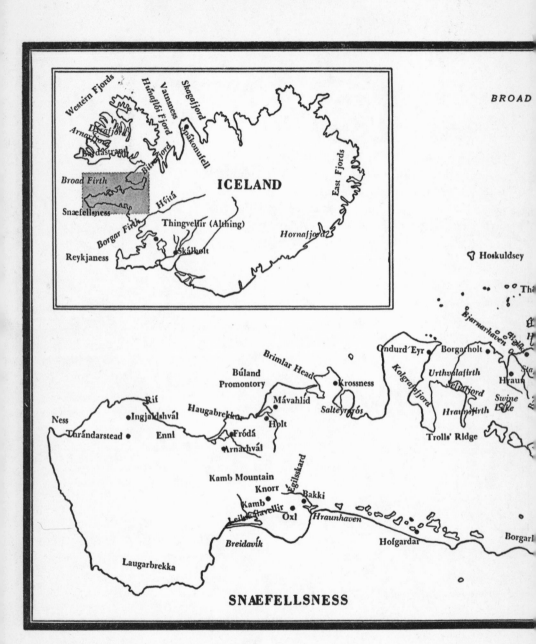

BROAD

ICELAND

Western Fjords

Húnaflói Fjord

Vatnsness

Skagafjord

Þsakonufell

East Fjords

Arnarfjord

Dýrafjord

Barðastrand

Bitrafjord

Broad Firth

Hvítá

Snæfellsness

Thingvellir (Althing)

Borgar Firth

Hornafjord

Reykjaness

Skálholt

♀ Hoskuldsey

Bjarnarhaven

Ondurd'Eyr

Borgarholt

Kolgrafafjord

Urthvalafirth

Seljafjord

Hraun

Brimlar Head

Búland
Promontory

Krossness

Saltcyrarós

Hraunsfirth

Swine
Lake

Rif

Máfahlíd

Trolls' Ridge

Ness

Ingjaldshvál

Haugabrekka

Þrándarstead

Enni

Holt

Fróðá

Arnarhvál

Kamb Mountain

Egilsskard

Knorr

Bakki

Kamb

Hraunhaven

Leikskála Brellir

Oxl

Breidavík

Hofgardar

Borgarl

Laugarbrekka

SNÆFELLSNESS